Hands-On Energy Therapy

for Horses and Riders

Hands-On Energy Therapy

for Horses and Riders

C L A R E   W I L D E

TRAFALGAR SQUARE PUBLISHING

North Pomfret, Vermont

Dedication: To Life!

First published in the United States of America in 1999 by
Trafalgar Square Publishing, North Pomfret, Vermont 05053

Printed and bound in Great Britain by Hillman Printers (Frome) Ltd

Co-published simultaneously in Great Britain by
Kenilworth Press Ltd, Addington, Buckingham, MK18 2JR

Disclaimer of Liability
The author and publisher shall have neither liability nor
responsibility to any person or entity with respect to any
loss or damage caused or alleged to be caused directly or
indirectly by the information contained in this book. While
the book is as accurate of the author can make it, there may
be errors, omissions, and inaccuracies.

ISBN 1-57076-135-3

Library of Congress Catalog Card Number 99-63903

Layout and typesetting by Kenilworth Press

Contents

Acknowledgments

Most importantly, thank you to my small, magical parents, Mike and Vicki, who selflessly brought me into this world, and knew they had somebody different on their hands, right from the start. My ever-excited mother gave me sensitivity, a delight in the simplest pleasures, and a joy of nature and the whole world. My father gave me tenacity, and generously provides the practical back-up way beyond parental duty, with visionary insight. Thank you, both – you had no training, but do a brilliant job, even when you're not sure why I'm doing what I do.

Thank you to my husband, Lee, who had no idea that his whole world would change from the moment he saw a girl standing on a balcony. He gives the shelter and support that a wild creature with her head in the clouds needs! We've been through much together: he is the rock in my storm.

Thanks to Linda, the most unconditionally supportive chum a girl could wish for – my, we've seen some changes!

To Mrs Lane, who made me aware of my 'gift'.

To Diana Fisher, Helen Philip, Jennifer Abbis, David at Insight – some who have shaped the process of my learning, and some who provide essential supervision and guidance. Thanks to my long-standing clients, human and otherwise. We learn and grow together. I offer a toast to Dr Gordon. To Julian Cope and Emily Bronte for inspiration.

To Lesley Gowers, for dealing with an author who insists on manifesting.

Finally, though they have never read a word I've written, thanks to the animals that share my life. The ever-faithful, smiling collies – Pip, my companion throughout the writing of this and my other books, who has been everywhere and done everything with me; and Dill, a true familiar, expert in vibrational medicine and the sheer joy of living. The amazing, April-born Anglo-Arabs – as always, dear April, with whom I have shared so many moments of pure bliss; and the sublime Ace, born on my birthday, with whom I hope to share many more.

Illustration credits

All photos are by Lee Milburn and Mike Lansdell. The superb line drawings and cover illustration are by Dianne Breeze.

Energy, Naturally!

Learning from nature – horses as teachers

The complementary therapy revolution, or re-evolution, flourishes as people seek a better way of living. This leads us to explore old ways – simple and effective, tried and trusted natural remedies. Granted, not all were perfect, but our new knowledge brings a fresh approach to those that work. Working to heal the bodies of both people and horses is an ancient practice; horses have been treated as companions, totems, guardians, and givers of strength since man has had a relationship with them. It is important to us to enjoy their companionship and, when there is a problem, it affects us as deeply as when our relationships with the people in our lives are troubled; sometimes more so, because there are barriers in our communication with animals.

Working with energy is a positive way to gain contact with your horse on a deep level, and working to heal our horses in this way is, I feel, an honour and a privilege. People who keep animals are often closer to nature, and those of us who keep horses are keen to find gentle, natural ways to care for our equine companions as well as ourselves. In this way, our horses often lead us to explore whole new areas of information which, without their prompting, we might never have found.

This animal-led exploration is true for many complementary thera-pists, and I am no different. My work in this field began primarily through competitive riding. The demands of competition prompt many careful riders to look below the surface, and to find ways forward when convention throws its hands up and says, 'It can't be done!' As a result of working with some less-than-straightforward horses, people often asked me to work with so-called 'difficult' horses. Working closely with horses that had all kinds of physical problems and often, behavioural quirks alongside, brought about a series of awakenings in my mind. Having always worked quietly and intuitively with the natural methods

I had been brought up to trust, I began to seek further training in complementary practice. This gave me the confidence to explore and experiment with new ways of combining new and old knowledge; and to take what I learned and add to it my own discoveries.

I saw many horses with problems, either through physical injuries, or 'memory-scars' leaving residual behavioural patterns. Riders, too, suffer from pain, nerves, stress, and fatigue; for competitive riders, the fitness demanded can put pressure on mind and body. Problems like these, as well as old, obscure and compounded injuries can prove difficult to treat by conventional methods as, technically, there is often nothing really 'wrong'! I found that this was where natural therapies shone, offering a variety of alternative ways of handling issues that had simply been given up on, or were being worked around. I do not set complementary and orthodox approaches against each other; I don't believe that there is a right or wrong approach, simply different ones. Some people take issue with the fact that complementary practitioners, particularly those in the healing arts, are not 'properly trained'. Although suitably qualified to work as I do, I see nothing 'wrong' with self-taught or intuitive practitioners, any more than there is anything 'right' about a string of examinations; these are simply issues of perception.

I have found that many people turn to complementary work, especially for treating their horses, because of the negative side-effects of drugs, which cannot be denied any less than can their benefits. Modern medicine has a more direct effect than many complementary techniques; but even 'safe' drugs (like penicillin) can harm, and bacteria are finding ways to adapt, by producing superbugs that can overcome drugs. Modern medicine also widely fails to address the emotional issues behind disease, which may be a large part of the cause, a fact attested to by doctors and psychologists worldwide. Because they are holistic, natural methods may have a more roundabout approach than those of modern medicine, but they have none of the dangerous side-effects.

When I wrote my first book, I realised that I was writing about many aspects of horse and rider that were normally never covered – or even considered. My main issue was the widespread fragmented approach to the well-being of people, horses and other animals. I chose to work with natural methods because they focus upon the wholeness of the individual, as opposed to taking a symptomatic approach. I also wanted to find a way of working that bridged the gap between behavioural training or learning, physical therapy, and internal medicine because for me, there is no way to separate these issues. I believe that the input into a body (both physically in terms of nourishment, and mentally through the senses in terms of experiences) and the resultant output (physical actions, behaviour and emotional reactions) are inextricably linked.

Papering over the cracks – a symptomatic view

Time and again I came across horses and other animals that, in spite of all kinds of physical treatments, mental/behavioural therapies or training, could just not shake off an old problem. This occurs most frequently in horses who, having been 're-schooled' or re-trained, repeat their old 'problematic' behaviour at a later date, simply because the root of the problem has never been addressed. The same can be true of people, particularly with stress or depression-related issues. Here, breakdown requires treatment, leading to a period of stability; but after a while, the same patterns can set in, leading to further breakdown. In humans and other animals, the problems have often started way back and it's important to release the root cause, instead of trying to overlay that root with new learning.

This 'overlay' approach can be likened to living in a house that is falling down, because the ground underneath it is subsiding. The movement in the foundations of the house leads the walls to shift and crumble. The first you know about it is that the wallpaper starts to tear and fall off the cracking walls. So, you redecorate, but because the walls keep moving, the wallpaper just keeps falling off! This, for me, epitomises the narrow field of focus of so many approaches to well-being: medicine, therapy of all kinds, training and teaching methods. Many such approaches attack the symptoms of a problem, seeking to overlay them with a new pattern – rather than trying to find what was really the cause of that set of symptoms and tackle it. Just like papering over the cracks.

My concerns about symptomatic approaches are founded on the belief that no living organism – human, horse, or any other – can truly be divided into a set of symptoms. The parts and systems of any body form a whole – they don't just exist in isolation. Without integrating the whole, it's very difficult to seek out and address an imbalance or negative issue that is causing a current problem.

I looked for a way to address the whole being, and release the root causes of the problems experienced by animals of all kinds – humans, horses, dogs, cats and many others. It struck me that, in people, problems caused by carrying the memory of an experience – what I call 'memory-scarring', are treated with counselling. The counselling process involves taking the 'presenting' problem (the apparent, obvious issue) and working back from there to find out what the cause is; what the deep-rooted issues behind this problem are. This is known as a 'talking cure'; talking being the main form of human communication. Because animals communicate by touch far more than verbally, we have to 'counsel' them physically; actually demonstrating on a physical level that it's OK, they're safe to release the old issues and move forward.

The root cause - physical, emotional or just being?

Many 'presenting' problems in people and horses first appear to be physical, but are in fact held in the mind or memory, and vice versa. Once again, I find that it is impossible to make a clear distinction between the two 'sets' of problem. After all, the 'mind', as an element of the brain, is simply another physical organ – a set of cells with its own energy and electrical impulses – so where is the distinction between the physical and the emotional? The boundaries blur completely where patterns of behaviour occur as a result of memory-scarring. Such behaviour is often linked to the fear of pain, rather than actual pain. In horses, the fear is of physical pain; in humans, the fear is often of emotional pain.

This way of holding information is simply the result of the way that animals learn (and here I include humans) by experience. If you put your hand in a fire, you learn that it burns and the pain teaches you to avoid a repeat performance. If you are extremely badly burned, your body might react with fear at an instinctive level – you feel afraid of fire (and remember, fear is an emotion – again, the blurring of distinction between physical and emotional). You might display your fear physically, with your body, by backing away from fires. As it turns out, nobody would blame you if you did! This pattern of stimulus-response conditioning also applies to purely emotional or intellectual factors. For example, if you go through a relationship break-up, it might make you wary of getting involved with another person for a while. There may not be any physical pain but, if you are really emotionally disturbed, you might not eat for a while, you might cry a lot – a physical display of emotion and again, the blurring of distinction between the two areas.

This stimulus-response model of learning 'by experience' applies, as far as we know, to the brain of every 'intelligent' living being. Therefore, when you apply it to horses, the pattern fits. Put a saddle on a horse's back which hurts because it doesn't fit, and he will instinctively learn to avoid the pain in one way or another. He has learned by experience, and the physical behaviour he exhibits gives clues as to his state of mind – again the blurring of distinction between physical and emotional. Being afraid of touching fire is a fairly useful pattern – but a horse being afraid of a saddle isn't very useful to his rider! With an understanding of the way we learn, and the aim of releasing negative patterns so that they don't reoccur, how can we communicate to our horse that a new saddle won't hurt like the old one did?

Our horse is letting us know his problem by communicating with us the only way he can – physically, because he has such a limited range of vocal communication – and we wouldn't understand him if he did vocalise to us anyway. But we can learn to understand what he is showing us physically, and the best way we can help him to release his problems is to show him, by communicating physically, that he doesn't need to be afraid of pain any more. Clearly, using the body and physical touch can be really valuable when it comes to communicating with not just horses, but all kinds of other animals – and even humans!

Touch as language

Touch, as a form of communication, is vastly underused by the human species in the western world. This may be primarily as a result of our social and cultural protocol – you don't go about touching people, especially people you don't know! We have come to rely so much on visual and auditory information, barely using our sense of touch in exchanging information between ourselves. This is particularly an issue when it comes to working with our horses, who use their bodies as their main means of conveying a message. The therapeutic value of touch for horses is vast – you only have to consider the fact that mutual grooming between horses lowers their heart-rate and blood pressure – yet, how often do we take the time to give our horses the luxury of this kind of inter-species bonding between us? Think, for yourself, about that feeling of really, really needing a hug, and how wonderful it feels when you finally receive it! This idea awakens the mind to clues about the relationship between physical touch and emotional release – that calming, comforting feeling produced by a physical activity, like a hug, which can so profoundly affect the emotions. But how can we use touch to release old, negative issues that are no longer useful – on an inter-linked physical/emotional level, and with many species?

I have always been a tactile person, and instinctively believed that somehow, the strength of simple contact was far, far greater than is generally accepted. In my work with 'difficult' horses, I spent a lot of time simply giving them exposure to human contact in an undemanding way. My aim was to try and demonstrate that we aren't all bad, and that people can be companions, not just taskmasters. Much of the time, I would simply talk to and touch the animals to encourage them to relax;

nothing more demanding than that. When I came across a healing touch therapy called Reiki (ray-key), I took training in it. This was exactly the 'touch' I had been looking for to help to release the root causes of issues across a range of species. I began to incorporate this healing energy therapy with my behavioural work, other vibrational medicines, natural methods and hitherto-gathered knowledge, to form an integrated, holistic, multi-species therapy.

Working with energy

Because touch is one of the most basic forms of communication – one of the five (acknowledged) senses – touch therapies like Reiki work deeply and powerfully. There are a number of theories about how energy is transmitted, and as there is so much research into this area of work, theories are being constantly developed. Everyone has seen the film 'Star Wars', where Luke Skywalker is taught about the mysterious 'force'! This is a great way to think of the vibrating energetic field that surrounds and is within everything living or otherwise: people, animals, plants, rocks, sound, waves of light – our world. This is the key to using energy as a therapy. Practitioners of healing energy therapy learn to draw in the 'force'; to tap the energy that is all around us, bring it into the body and project it through the hands. Drawing in and projecting energy is a practice that has been included in medicine since ancient times, to raise energy levels and keep the energy flow around the body free. Practices such as Tai Chi also seek to produce the same effect, and in the East, masters of many martial arts also work to heal others with energy. As some say that the origins of Eastern medicine using energy projection are said to date back three or four thousand years, man is likely always to have recognised the therapeutic strength of touch. The subtle exchange of energy between the recipient of the energy and the practitioner – sending in the positive, replacing and recharging the negative – can be deeply therapeutic.

One way to think of this process is like a two-way telephone conversation – through the miracles of modern technology, you dial a number which is, effectively, a code matching the location you want to reach. When your friend answers the call, you exchange information and tell each other your news, and maybe some of your troubles. You put down the receiver, and voila! You feel wonderful – uplifted, and far better about life. Energy therapy is thought to work in the same way, by matching the vibration of energy in the recipient's body – the location you want to reach – and exchanging energy to release, refresh, rebalance and revitalise.

There are all kinds of theories, scientific and otherwise, about how energy works to heal the body, some of which I will explain in this book. As one works with energy, however, one simply sees the effects and ceases to question the process behind it. Suffice to say here that exchanging energy at such a deep level has a profoundly relaxing effect on the recipient, enabling the release of physical and emotional tensions, old patterns and blockages. In this way, healing energy therapy can tackle and release the deeply rooted causes of so many problems that have become hidden, buried or forgotten. This can be an uplifting and liberating process for humans and animals alike. Sometimes, perhaps because of the way that input from the senses (in the form of cellular activity) is processed into images and sensations within the brain, a practitioner can feel something of the recipient's troubles, or gain a sense of the history behind their problems. I find this to be true whether the recipient is human or equine. An experienced practitioner can also feel places in the body where the flow of energy is disrupted or blocked. On a physical level, injuries place extra strain on the surrounding tissues and, in the long-term, the body adapts either by altering its physical way of moving or behaviour. Energy therapy can release the pain held within, and encourage healing of bodily tissue. In this way, disturbances are re-balanced, keeping the flow of energy around the body clear, strong and healthy.

I do not suggest that healing energy therapy is a miraculous cure-all, or a quick fix for every problem that we, or our horses, have. However, healing with energy serves to stimulate and speed up the body's own natural healing process. I have seen tangible benefits as a result of treatment time and time again. In people, this is often put down to the placebo effect; hardly a good argument where horses are concerned. For those who need the support of scientific evidence, there is plenty of it, and that body of evidence is growing. Projection of energy can effect the haemoglobin component of the recipient's blood cells. It can change the brainwaves of the recipient into a low-amplitude alpha state of calmness and relaxation, increase blood flow (making oxygen more available to the tissues), and speed the healing of injuries[1]. The beneficial results of working with energy are thought to exceed those gained through acupuncture, now a widely accepted practice throughout the Western world. There is a vast body of research being made into energy and even modern physicists no longer see matter as matter, but rather as a density of energy, with the whole world composed of different patterns or vibrational frequencies of energy.

Healing with energy has also been the subject of experiments upon plants, and has improved their growth substantially – a plant can hardly be said to be subject to the placebo effect. However, placebo effect or no, any benefit is positive. The placebo effect itself is the subject of much discussion, and it is thought to be related to positive visualisation, perhaps as a result of auto-suggestion and intent upon the part of the patient.[2] This may be as a result of the trust in the therapy, which is something that those who work with healing have – a trust in the energy that they are using. The idea of trust, or intent, has even been proposed as a form of energy projection.

Holistic healing – a way forward

Anyone can learn to use energy therapy, and work on their own body or their own horse. With horses and riders, this can be applied to everything from physical injuries to behavioural issues and the vast range of problems that have roots in both, or neither end, of this spectrum. Energy is used as a key to unlock negative issues and to move forward, incorporating new ways of learning for both horse and rider. I work with horses and riders together because again, for me, there is an inextricable link between symptomatic behaviour in one and causal behaviour in the other. When a horse begins to 'do something', the rider often becomes stressed and confused, inducing further tension in the horse, exacerbating the behaviour, and so on in a downward spiral! Many traditional trainers of horses and riders are still papering over the cracks – if the horse is resistant, work it! A holistic approach would be to find out why the horse is resistant, and work to heal the cause of the problem.

One main reason for working with horse and rider as a team, especially where physical problems in horses are concerned, is because riders are the cause of the majority of horses' problems; a fact that's hard to swallow for many people. However, for those prepared to look honestly and objectively at ways to improve the situation, this can be the key to unlocking the root of so many long-held, recurring issues and moving forward. This, in turn, can halt the downward spiral of stress exacerbating problems and turn it about, forming an upward spiral – where horse and rider become steadily happier and more relaxed with each other. I receive questions and requests for help from riders for themselves and their horses, for all kinds of other animals, and other people not even remotely connected with horses, but who want to find a new way of clearing old issues. Many of these are on the downward spiral and are looking for a way back up. I work with, and teach many people how to use energy therapy for themselves. For horses and riders, it is all about using energy to bring into balance the horse and rider as an alliance or unit. If we can establish a deeper understanding of, and contact with, our own bodies and those of our horses, we can find the basis of the harmony with our horses that we all strive to reach.

The flat-earth society

People who work in new and innovative ways are often open to criticism. Innovative thinkers are, by their nature, often working ahead of their time and are often criticised by those who are unwilling or unready to move with progress. Usually, I put this kind of reaction down to the fact that it's easier to poke fun at something than learn about it. People tend to shy away from things that challenge their personal beliefs or belief-systems. In other words, it's fear of change, or sticking with what people know that makes them so quick to fear the new or strange. After all, people once thought the earth was flat!

I find it hard to understand how there can be argument against healing bodywork of any kind. It's non-invasive and can never do any harm, so why not use it – particularly in situations where all else has failed? Everyone accepts the comforting value of a hug, or the relaxing feeling of a good massage, and we only have to watch our horses with each other to see how much they use their bodies and sense of touch. For me, working with energy is not just invaluable, it's essential – both as a means of helping ourselves and the people around us, and particularly to help our horses and other animals, who communicate so predominantly with their bodies. To all those sceptics I would ask – how many of you have never 'kissed something better' for a child, or instinctively clasped your hands over a fresh pain or injury? And have you ever wondered why?

Where do you begin?

Many of you will already be working with energy in some way, either through training or naturally, and if so, you will be able to make instant use of the practical information given in this book. However, if you wish to undertake formal training in using energy therapy, advice on finding a teacher and being 'attuned' in Reiki is given in Chapter 7. Some of you may unwittingly possess the ability to project energy, and whether this is true or not, there will be no harm in trying out the treatment procedures on your horse, yourself or a friend.

What is Energy Therapy?

Energy – fuel for life

What makes a body tick? People have pondered this age-old question and come up with a whole range of different answers. The fictional Dr Frankenstein, no less, made a creature of his own and kick-started it with a combination of electricity and human body fluid. It is generally agreed that there is some kind of energy that makes the body begin functioning and, at the point of death, cease functioning. There are many names for this energy and people think of it in various different ways, according to how it best fits in with their own belief systems – as coming from God, the earth, the universe, or as an electrical field. It's easy to think of the body as an energy system, but harder to see that there can be an abundance of energetic force around us in the world if it isn't somehow 'housed' in a body.

Currently, one of the main schools of thought is that the way of using energy as a healing therapy works by exchanging a 'charge' between (but not from) the hands of the practitioner and the body of the recipient. The best way to understand this is to think about the fundamental fact that everything – you, me, the table I'm sitting at – is made up of tiny atoms, the basis for all substance. By their very nature, atoms are never still but are constantly vibrating, and that vibration has a frequency, charge or energy all its own, creating an energy 'field' around each group of atoms making up a whole object. That 'object' might be a human, a horse, a plant, a stone, a liquid. Everything in our world vibrates at its own frequency, from rays of light, to waves of sound, to the energy of our own bodies, to the ground beneath our feet.

Physicists now believe that everything in the world is composed of energy; that atmospheric or ambient energy is a real and unseen force, just as gravity is. This energy exists all around us and, as well as flowing through organisms, can be drawn in, to have a tangible effect on the body. Some call it 'bioenergy' and explain that it exists as short-wave vibrations that can't be seen (just as there are waves of energy that vibrate at frequencies beyond the range of human perception, like high-pitched sound and waves of light, or radio and television signals). As this ambient energy is drawn into the body, it flows along pathways called **meridians** and through energy centres called **chakras,** as well as surrounding our physical bodies in a field sometimes called the **aura.** The energetic field surrounding the body has been photographed using Kirlian photography, proving that it's a real phenomenon. Some sensitive people can feel and see it.

The name you choose to give this life-force energy depends upon your culture and background. In Chinese medicine, it is called **Qi,** or **Chi,** and in Japan, **Ki,** in Hindu, **Prana.** Many cultures place great importance on this invisible connecting energy, and widely document its use in healing. English-speaking languages currently lack a word for it, perhaps because the concept is not a familiar one in our culture. In its most basic terms, the energy level of the body, if either low or restricted, renders a person or animal more vulnerable to illness. When the energy is flowing freely, the body is more likely to stay healthy.

Where one learns to work with it, energy can prove an incredibly powerful healer of our minds and bodies. Drawing in and projecting this energy may be an unfamiliar idea to most Westerners. However, most of us are now well aware of the 'energetic' principle of treatment with homeopathy: that of matching the energetic vibration of the medicine with that of the patient's illness, stimulating the body into producing more energy and healing itself. The same principle applies to all kinds of vibrational medicine: aromatherapy, the use of herbs, crystals, colour, sound, and touch or healing with energy. The vibrational levels of the energy field of people projecting energy during therapeutic treatments have even been measured with sensitive instruments under laboratory conditions. As we have been applying vibrational medicine to our own bodies for years, and we are already using so many natural therapies for our horses, perhaps now it is time to think about the benefits of working to heal our horses with energy.

Seeing isn't believing

The idea of the passage of energy within and around the body is the basis of many therapies, including acupuncture, shiatsu, magnetic therapy, healing using machines such as lasers and pulsed electromagnetic fields, and bodywork of all kinds. However, when it comes to understanding something as subtle as simply laying on the hands to project energy, people often ask, 'If I can't see it, how do I know it's

THE HORSE'S MAIN MERIDIANS

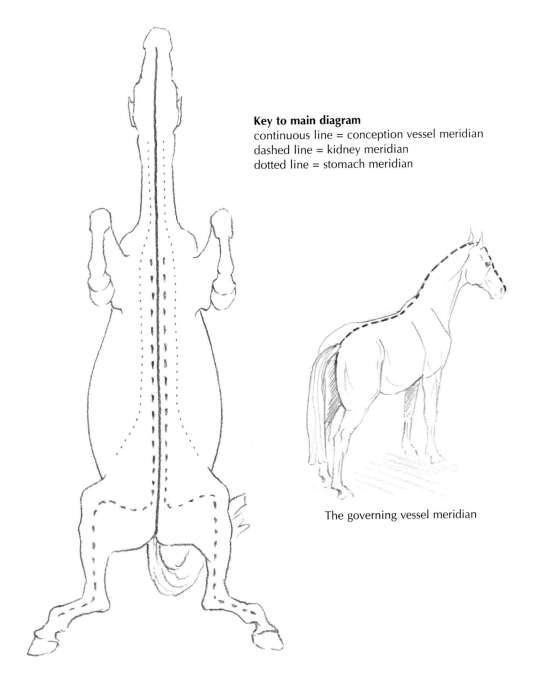

Key to main diagram
continuous line = conception vessel meridian
dashed line = kidney meridian
dotted line = stomach meridian

The governing vessel meridian

THE SEVEN MAIN CHAKRAS

IN MAN

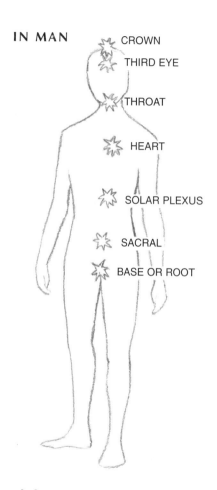

CROWN
THIRD EYE
THROAT
HEART
SOLAR PLEXUS
SACRAL
BASE OR ROOT

IN THE HORSE

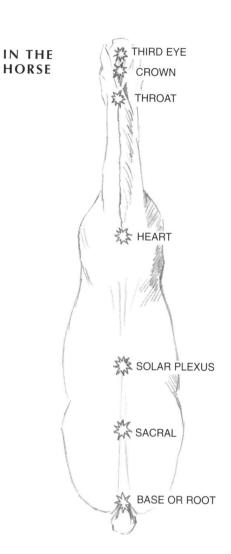

THIRD EYE
CROWN
THROAT
HEART
SOLAR PLEXUS
SACRAL
BASE OR ROOT

The chakras

- CROWN – violet – spiritual, higher self
- THIRD EYE – indigo – wisdom, vision
- THROAT – blue – communication
- HEART – green – love, relationships with others
- SOLAR PLEXUS – yellow – emotions
- SACRAL – orange – energy, personal strength
- BASE or ROOT – red – grounding, instincts

Locating the horse's chakras

- CROWN: between the ears, at the poll
- THIRD eye: on the forehead, slightly above the level of the eyes
- THROAT: where the jawbone meets the neck (think of a throatlatch)
- HEART: withers, chest between forelegs, girth area
- SOLAR PLEXUS: at the back of the saddle (end of the ribcage)
- SACRAL: the point of the sacro-iliac joint
- BASE or ROOT: base of the spine, or top of the tail

real?' To this I would ask in reply, is the world of a blind person any less real than that of a sighted person? Clearly, a blind or visually impaired person does not have to see the world to know that it exists by experiencing it through their other senses. None of us can see the wind, but we can feel it; we can't see electricity, but it powers the equipment we use every day of our lives.

Perhaps the best example of how little vision actually has to do with the reality of our world and the way our bodies function, is the phenomenon known as gravity. Gravity is often defined as a 'force'; it is produced by the influence of the planets, and you can't see or feel it in any recognisable way during your everyday life. However, if it didn't keep us pinned to the ground, we'd have to evolve a whole new way of living! This opens up the way we can think of and understand energy. People generally cease to question the validity of being able to see the energy once they experience the effect of a healing energy treatment and, more particularly, see the effect it has on their horses. An animal responding to an 'invisible' therapy is surely the best way to counter any argument about the idea that the effects of a treatment must have been 'all in the mind'.

The idea that something has to be seen for us to believe it, is a symptom of the way that we have been conditioned to think and act – to accept primarily visual and auditory cues. This conditioning is encouraged by the bombardment of mass-produced, visual and auditory media as stimulation for our senses throughout our everyday lives. Anything that doesn't fit our conditioned mould – a feeling that we can't explain, from some other source of cellular sensual input – is thought of as odd, confusing and strange. Perhaps the question should be, 'If I can't see it, what sense *can* I experience it with?' If you accept that horses communicate with emphasis on different senses, it is easy to see that our hang-ups about what is normal or acceptable are simply a question of the limits imposed by the rules we live by. It's a little like the fact that the British drive on the left – it doesn't mean it's impossible to drive on the right, it's simply how things are in Britain.

Horses, however, don't have the intellectual processes surrounding acceptable behaviour in the same way that we do. They are far more open to influences from their environment – as are children, before conditioning sets in. Because of this, a therapy that people may find hard to understand is often best experienced first-hand through the medium of their own horse, who is incapable of 'pretending' or 'imagining' it can feel something. Many riders come to energy therapy through first having asked a practitioner to treat their horses. When they see the sheer relaxation under treatment and the beneficial after-effects that their horses experience, they're often queuing up to experience the feeling for themselves.

Thinking with our senses

Before we humans had got to the point of inventing so much crazy social protocol and conditioning, before we lived almost exclusively in towns, we were much more like other animals – closer to nature and our own environment. How often do you, in the hurry to get to work on time in the morning, stand still, look up at the sky, drink in the colours, smells and sounds, and really feel your own surroundings? If you turn your horse loose in a field and watch his response to the morning, the first thing he will do is use all his senses to experience his environment. Perhaps, as riders and handlers of horses, we are a little closer to the influences of nature than those who don't spend time outside or with animals. When our ancient ancestors lived on the land, without the clutter and distraction we have today, they would have had no option but to notice the colour of the sky and the smells and sounds around them – and how this sensual input made their minds and bodies feel. Their lives were governed by the ebb and flow of nature, the source of all they needed.

Where the land and the environment felt good (perhaps through the pull of the earth's own energy), they built their settlements and temples of dedication; they gathered for meetings and worship of the natural forces that governed their world. These energies have been symbolised in different ways by many different cultures – the Chinese dragon, the Aboriginal spiral, the Native American serpent – but such slight variations of form and pattern are all expressions of the same feeling of natural force. Perhaps what our ancestors knew has been lost with the changes in our culture and lifestyle. Perhaps the senses that we once used to perceive our world, in the way that our horses do, have receded with lack of use. There are many pointers to the fact that we may once have been able to feel, or are still at some level aware of, far more than is generally consciously acknowledged. These are ideas to bear in mind if you are interested in working with energy for yourself. One of these 'clues' to a deeper understanding of energy is the way that we react to physical pain. What's the first thing you do if you stub your toe, or bang your head? You place your hand over the area where the pain is, and hold on. Why?

For the majority of the population, who are not using energy to heal the affected area, there is nothing that placing a hand over the area can do to lessen the pain. For anyone able to make energy available to the

ENERGY SYMBOLS FROM DIFFERENT CULTURES

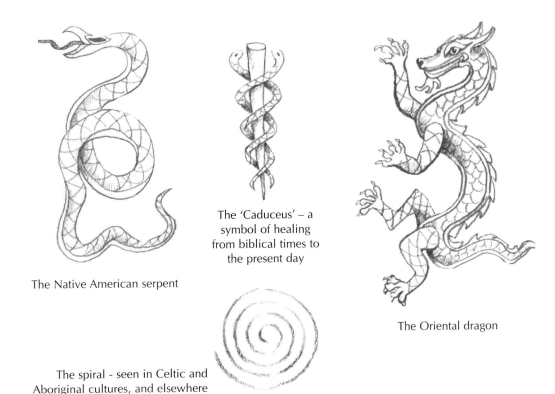

The 'Caduceus' – a symbol of healing from biblical times to the present day

The Native American serpent

The Oriental dragon

The spiral - seen in Celtic and Aboriginal cultures, and elsewhere

area, pain and swelling can be lessened and the injury encouraged to heal. Is it possible, therefore, that this is a 'race memory' – an action which, perhaps, was automatic to our ancestors? Maybe, experiencing the natural forces in their world far more closely than we do, our forebears could make energy available through their hands, and in placing them over the body, could work in this way to heal. It is also entirely possible that our horses are more aware of the forces of natural energy than we are. Much of the time, people who learn to use healing energy therapy say, 'It feels so natural – like I should have always been able to do it.' Perhaps once, we all could. Many of the riders whom I teach to use energy on their own horses say that it's exactly what they were looking for, and how right it feels to be working to heal their horses with their hands.

The energy therapy which I learned, called 'Reiki' is said to have evolved from the healing art practised by one ancient culture, the

Buddhists. Reiki is a Japanese word used to describe the concept of using life-force energy as a healing therapy (the 'ki' part of the word means energy). There are many ancient cultures throughout the world that retain the ability to work with energy. Such cultures accept, as part of their everyday life, the ability to be able to heal the bodies and minds of those around them, both human and animal. Often the role of healer is given to a medicine man, shaman, witch, or religious leader. Healing knows no boundaries of culture or species and, like the patterns used to symbolise its energy, in practice it varies little between one people and the next.

In such cultures, animals are often given high status and regarded as the physical embodiment of the mysterious powers of nature; particularly horses, which are, or have been, so valuable as both transport and food. Members of tribes and peoples across the world are named after animals and have animals as their guides. This tradition even continued in the West until a century or two ago, when witches' familiars (usually cats and dogs) were burned with them – although I don't know of any witches whose familiars were horses! In those days, anyone having an unusually close relationship with an animal was thought to have mysterious powers and was persecuted as a result.

Energy as information

Another clue to the possibility that we can actually sense far more than we acknowledge, is the language we use to describe what we feel. For example, when you first walk into a building, even before you consciously register how you feel about the decorative taste, the shape of the room, and so on – you make a decision about how you feel about the environment. This may, in fact, be as a result of the subtle effect of the décor – all colours have a vibration and each component within that environment goes to make up the total vibration, or set of vibrations, experienced by our own energy field as we enter that space. But this judgement – I like it; I don't like it – occurs regardless of such superficialities as colour. If you view a prospective new house, you may decide to buy it even though you want to redecorate! In this way, it is possible that our 'gut feeling' is based purely upon the interaction of our own energy field and that of the space we encounter.

This happens with people, too – at a deep level, we make quite an instant decision about whether we 'feel comfortable' with someone or not. 'Feel comfortable'? Have we actually 'felt' the person? Given the protocols surrounding touch in our modern society, it is highly unlikely! We use expressions like, 'we were really sparking off each other', or 'he was really grating on me' to describe the way that we feel about somebody – physical words to describe something that we haven't physically felt at all. Again, these words describe the feeling of how our own energy interacts with that of the other individual.

An energy field full of soft, gentle, positive, calming energy has a soothing effect upon our own, which is why we often feel so comfortable, happy and calm around our horses or other animals. An energy field throwing off darts and spikes of anger and negativity, that begin to lodge within the field of our own energy, gives us a nasty, uncomfortable feeling. The way in which we process this information in our brains has an influence upon the language we use to express the feelings we experience.

This can also be thought of as one explanation for the way that animals react to us. I know horses that react to the same person in two completely different ways, on the strength of something as subtle as the way that person is thinking. In my own yard I have experimented with this during my work with rehabilitating horses, being prompted to do so by one horse that seemed to be incredibly unpredictable. I originally experimented with walking around the corner to his box (stall) whilst frowning or smiling, but without speaking or altering the rest of my body at all. Later, on discovering that this really did make a difference to the horse's reaction, I dropped the facial cues and worked on approaching with either a clenched or loose jaw. Later still, I repeated the same tests simply thinking relaxed, happy thoughts or thinking tense, angry thoughts. Each time, the horse reacted accordingly. It is likely that the thoughts in our minds prompt our bodies to display a set of very subtle clues, perhaps evincing just a little tension in our arms or the way we walk; all of which is worth considering as you ask yourself why your horse is snappy today.

The physical body – emotion made real

Our energy fields as adults can be quite strong and closed to the influence of others. They may, however, be more sensitive and open to surrounding influences, as are the energy fields of animals and children. If you think again about how it feels to be with someone who gives you a delightfully energised, positive feeling, the words they say and physical actions they make can have a profound effect upon how you feel. This is said to be due to the energetic forms of thought and words as they attach themselves to your own energy, and are taken in, affecting your energy. You feel bigger, stronger, more positive – wonderful! For example, 'He thinks I'm gorgeous. I feel gorgeous. I feel great! Look out, world!' You walk down the road with a spring in your step and a smile on your face – and full of energy. Just think about how it feels when you first see your horse in the morning, and greet each other – a really enjoyable, pleasing, uplifting feeling – you go to mix his feed with a smile.

However, spend some time with someone exuding negative energy, and their looks, actions and words can affect your own energy field in a negative way – causing disruptions, like a grain of sand in a soft oyster's shell. These 'minuses', fed by our own beliefs, become stronger and more influential (just as 'positives' can) so that we are just as deeply affected by them. 'He said I was horrible. I am horrible. I'm a horrible person and everybody hates me...' Eventually, the effect can become physical: affecting our behaviour, making us slump, frown, or even cry. If your horse swings to bite you as you greet him in the morning, the 'feeling' you get (if you dodged the teeth!) is one of upset, and you hunch up and shuffle off to mix his feed with a frown. This idea, that of the physical body being a manifestation of our emotions and the information received through sensual input, is one of the main principles of healing with energy.

The energy fields of animals, children and babies, unable to employ the intellectual safeguards that we do as adults with experience, are wide open to influence. This is why so many problems begin in early life for both horses and people. As an infant, we have so few people to shape our worlds and we place such great importance upon those who do. Our horses have equally few people to influence their lives – usually just one or two people. Over the years, the effects of the negative and positive influences placed within the wide-open energy fields of infants and animals can come to colour the whole world of that individual.

Your horse might not know whether you're telling him he's gorgeous or horrible because he doesn't understand your words. However, the way you feel about what you're saying will be expressed by the tones and body language that you use. With kind words, we use a gentle tone and a soft, caressing touch. With angry words, we use a harsh tone and draw our bodies up aggressively. After a while, your horse will become used to the feeling you or anybody else gives him; and will begin to react accordingly. This just goes to show what a responsibility it is to be in a position of influence, particularly with children and animals that so readily accept what is given to them. Perhaps this is also food for thought about the way we influence the people we encounter in our everyday lives!

The theory of influencing the energy of another individual is one explanation of the way that the physical body acts almost as a manifestation, or symptom of what affects us mentally. It can also account for how it may be possible to use energy to release and heal the whole body. A more scientific approach may be helpful to others and my past study of neuroscience has given me another 'model' of energetic transmission around the body. Neuroscience is the study of the way that information, in the form of sensory input, affects the brain and thus, the body. It would take another book to explain this work in detail, but I will briefly give some information here.

Neuroscience and energy – a rough guide

We all know that the living body, human or equine, is made up of a vast number of living cells. Cells known as 'receptors' are found all over the body, for example in the skin, the ears and the eyes. In the skin, these are 'mechanoreceptors', or cells that are sensitive to stimulation by touch. Receptors can also be called sensory cells, because they are used in receiving and processing the information that we generally describe as coming from the 'senses'. Sensory cells convert the energy they receive into electrical signals, and can send a graded scale of signal, according to the information received. These electrical signals are carried to the brain across the synapses, which are the gaps between the receptor and the nerve cells or neurons. The generated signal moves across the synapse to stimulate the nerve cell, which in turn carries the signal to the brain. In horses, information received through the skin is said to be concerned mainly with temperature regulation. However, when you consider that the skin is the largest and most sensitive organ in the body – and think about how much you have learned through sensations on your skin – this gives you some idea of how much information may be received through touch.

Different areas of the brain are made up of clumps of neuron endings leading from all over the body, including the sensory cells. In this way, it can be said that the images we experience through receiving information about smell, light, touch and so on, are 'stored' or 'processed' in the brain. The brain is also made up of neurons that affect different parts of the body, such as motor neurons which *affect* movement, and neurons affecting the function of the body including lymphatic, circulatory and endocrine systems. In the simplest of terms, cells influencing behaviour, such as motor neurons, are affected by electrical potential from synapses at either end. For example, an impulse travelling from the brain down a neuron to a muscle can signal it to move. Perhaps this can begin to explain how making energy available through healing therapy can so profoundly affect the physical body as well as the emotions. This

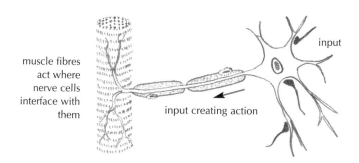

A motor neuron cell acts on the muscle, causing it to contract. In simple terms, input travels across the cell, initiating action.

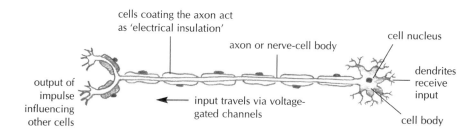

A neuron of the central nervous system.

is a particularly interesting idea in terms of working with animals, where their behaviour is not surrounded with the intellectual complexity of our own, but operates on a far more instinctive, physical level.

The electrical charge of individual cells can actually be measured using a voltameter. Charges are carried through the neurons and other cells via the fluids that make up the body. The fluid or 'chemical solution' contained within the cells is different to the fluid surrounding them. The ions within those solutions, for example sodium ions or potassium ions, carry a positive or negative charge and as such attract or repel the ions around them. When the concentration of ions charged one way reaches such a level that it begins to attract a flow of ions of the opposite polarity, the ions move across channels in the cell membranes. Some of these channels are even 'voltage-gated', so that ions will move across cell membranes according to the level of voltage reached by the ionic charge. All of this theory is fine, but it is important to understand that the body itself is an energy system, and that sensory input and output is processed within it in the form of energetic charge.

Using energy to heal

It is possible to positively influence the energy fields of the bodies around us, particularly our horses, by using energy as a therapy. We can learn to draw in and make energy available to other bodies, be they human, other animals or whatever. In this way, we can help to move blockages, to recharge negativity and to replenish the energy of a body that has become run-down, sick or ill, stimulating the body to heal itself. Because of the inextricable relationship between physical sickness and emotional issues, healing with energy addresses the whole system, rather than just a part of it, including the energy field around the physical body, where problems start before being manifested physically.

On a physical level, energy works to heal the whole individual, and not simply by masking or eliminating a symptom, e.g. putting a plaster or bandage over a cut, or drying up a runny nose, or bringing down a temperature. Where the emotions are concerned, energy works to heal the issues held within the organ or set of cells called the brain; as well as the way that those issues have come to affect the physical body, in terms of behavioural patterns. This works through recharging the energy field of the recipient's body, strengthening it so that negative energy, disruptions or blockages can be thrown off before they become a problem. Energy also affects the behaviour and emotions on a cellular level; in that information, through input from the senses, is processed and held in the cells of the brain. In this way, energy therapy can help to release long-held emotional patterns.

Working with energy leaves the body of both recipient and practitioner feeling refreshed and recharged. It is a myth surrounding healing that the practitioner gets tired. This is simply not the case where one has learned to tune in and work with the energy that is available to all of us. Such exhaustion may occur where people are sending out their own energy and leaving themselves depleted; but this is not advisable or indeed healthy to the healer or the recipient. How can anyone being treated be assured of receiving pure, unadulterated energy if it's been sitting in someone else's body first?! Working with universally available energy is an uplifting and energising experience, as the body of the person acting as a conduit or channel receives some energy as it passes through them on its way to the recipient's body.

To summarise the ideas and concepts described here:

- Energy flows through the physical body through pathways called meridians, and energy centres called chakras. All animals have meridians and chakras.
- Energy also flows around the body in a field, sometimes called the aura, which has even been photographed. All animals have an aura.
- Energy nourishes the body.
- When the flow of energy is disrupted, it affects the way the body functions.
- Energy is responsive to thoughts, instincts and feelings.
- Negative energy can become lodged within an individual's energy field and cause a disruption of flow.
- Healing energy therapy works by flowing through the physical body and energy field, recharging with positive energy and raising the energetic vibration, causing negative energy to fall away. In so doing, the energy pathways are cleared and healed, re-establishing a full and healthy flow.

Healing Hands –
A History of Reiki

One healing energy therapy that is widely taught and used in the West is called 'Reiki'. Anyone can learn Reiki to benefit their own bodies and those of their horses; it may be interesting to those thinking of doing so to hear a little about it here. I do not claim to be a Reiki purist, but since much of my work is based upon healing energy therapy, I feel it only fair to give the art of Reiki due credit.

Reiki has a colourful story behind it, but it is not known how much of the story is true and how much of it is embellishment, designed to make an Eastern practice more acceptable to Westerners. There is a Traditional Reiki group, who have had access to teachings and notes kept by those who learned from the originator of Reiki, and they claim that almost none of the story as it is taught in the West is true. What you decide to believe is up to you.

A history of Reiki

The man responsible for Reiki as it is largely taught today was Mikao Usui. He was born in Japan in 1865 into a family who followed Buddhist traditions. Usui is said to have fostered the idea that man's ability to heal others had largely been lost through lack of use. This concept so fascinated him that he set off on a quest in search of this forgotten knowledge. He travelled widely throughout Japan and (some say) Tibet, visiting monasteries and consulting religious leaders and spiritual teachers. Eventually his findings led him to undertake a twenty-one day fast on a holy mountain. On the twenty-first day he literally 'saw the light' and received the answer to his quest.

It seems that this story about Usui's quest originated with a Reiki student named Mrs Takata. Takata studied under one of Usui's original students, Chujiro Hayashi, and she was responsible for taking Reiki to America. Mrs Takata has always maintained that Usui rediscovered Reiki, as opposed to developing it as a practice himself. It is thought that she gave the Reiki stories to her own students to make Reiki more acceptable to them. She has also said that Usui was a doctor, but there is no evidence to support this. It is more likely that his status as 'sensei', meaning master or teacher, has been westernised into the word 'doctor'.

Several years ago, two Reiki practitioners from Canada visited some of the students taught by Hayashi, one of Usui's original students, who had quite a different story to tell. They say that around 1900, Usui created a system of natural healing based upon ancient Buddhist healing traditions, Taoist energy practices (whereby the practitioner learns to draw in energy and project it to others) and Eastern medicine using the meridians, or energy pathways of the body. Usui is supposed to have attended a Buddhist monastery from an early age, where he developed an interest in healing and researched medicine and healing in libraries there.

He spent many years searching for a way to connect to healing energy, and went to Koriyama to meditate at a temple, where he underwent a twenty-one day period of purification and meditation. Usui then spent seven years in the poor quarter of Kyoto and in 1922 he opened a school of healing in Tokyo. Here, he taught many students how to draw in and project energy for healing, including around sixteen students whom he trained as teachers, before his death four years later.

The ancient origins of healing

The original work taught and practised by Usui is built around a traditional healing practice that has been used for thousands of years in the Far East. One of the main principles of this work is that when a person becomes seriously out of balance, techniques like projecting energy are used in an attempt to cure them.

Reiki is a generic term in Japan, used to describe many types of healing with energy. It is not exclusive to the system of healing based on Usui's work, which is often called the 'Usui system of natural healing'. The Usui system has evolved and, in its current state, it is much more organised and structured than the simple, flexible, intuitive method practised originally. Many teachers have made changes to the way they teach Reiki, which accounts for the variation between one line of teaching and another. There is even talk of trademarking 'Reiki', particularly in America.

Chujiro Hayashi

Hayashi, one of Usui's original students, was a retired naval officer. He learned Reiki from Usui in 1925, at the age of forty-seven. Before Usui died, his method of healing concentrated on applying energy to seven points on the body related to the main meridians. Hayashi went on to develop and formalise the method, opening a clinic in Tokyo and keeping detailed records of the treatments given. He created a complex set of twenty-four standard hand positions, which were used by several practitioners at a time to work on one patient. His approach to healing with energy was a very 'medical', regimented one. He also formalised the process of teaching energy therapy to others into a three-level system, and used to train people who volunteered to work with him for a given length of time.

One of Hayashi's students was Mrs Takata, and another a man named Tatsumi, from whom much of this information has been received.

Hawayo Takata

Mrs Takata trained under Hayashi, and was largely responsible for bringing Reiki to America and so the Western world. Mrs Takata met Hayashi through his clinic, having originally attended it to receive Reiki treatments for her own illnesses – she was considered to be terminally ill at the time. She is said to have been so impressed by the strength of the healing energy she received under treatment that, when she recovered, she wanted to learn to use Reiki for herself. Hayashi began training her in 1936 and, by 1938, Mrs Takata had learned enough to teach others the system of working with energy; she was the thirteenth and last Reiki teacher whom Hayashi initiated.

Mrs Takata moved to America to remarry and there she introduced the idea of training students in the art of Reiki and charging for it. Prior to this, it is thought that no money exchanged hands at all. Hayashi used to train people as they worked alongside him and it is believed that Usui did the same. When Mrs Takata first taught Reiki to others in America, she charged $10,000 to train to teacher level, because she maintained that this is what she had paid Hayashi to buy the right to teach Reiki outside Japan. Between 1970 and her death in 1980, Mrs Takata initiated twenty-two Reiki teachers. These have taught others and since 1980, Reiki has spread rapidly. It is now practised worldwide and countless numbers of new students learn Reiki every day.

There is quite a movement throughout the Reiki community to bring the cost of training down, and make healing with energy available to everyone who wishes to receive it or learn about it. The main issue to bear in mind is that working with energy is a priceless gift; in paying for treatments or training, we are simply paying the person whose time we are taking up, so that they can make a living. With this in mind, you should be careful when approaching a practitioner or teacher who charges very high prices, or who claims that their treatments are somehow 'better' or 'more powerful' than others. There is also a small element of therapists who claim that the whole issue is very mysterious and only the chosen few should be trained in it! Unfortunately, Reiki has become something of a commodity and, because it can be learned so quickly and easily, there will always be those who have a commercial, rather than ethical or responsible approach to it.

The meaning of 'Reiki'

It is often taught today that the word Reiki means a universal energy that has some kind of consciousness, or wisdom. All kinds of literal and speculative translations have been made of the characters and the word itself. However, the original use of the word was found in a text of Usui's, showing the affirmations used by his group of students. It is believed that, as Usui used it and as it would have been meant by the Taoists, the word means 'spirit' or 'spiritual'. Tatsumi, who trained under Hayashi, said that, as quoted in one of the affirmations given to Usui's students, it meant: 'the Usui spiritual [Reiki] method to change your mind and body for the better'.

Natural healing for horse and rider

However it was developed, the practice of healing with energy is now widespread and is taught throughout the Western world. One of the important issues to bear in mind is that Usui's way of working is said to have been very simple and instinctive. He placed his hands in just a few places on the body – the head, eyes, collarbone, and upper body, and he worked intuitively. However, his system of healing has come to be taught and practised in all kinds of different, often elaborate ways. Some people prefer a regimented approach, using equipment and different paraphernalia. Where horses are concerned, however, I feel that a simple and instinctive approach is best and I believe that there should be no 'tools' necessary when working with something as natural as energy. The way that Reiki is practised today varies widely, but the fact remains that all practitioners are working with energy to heal the body.

Energy therapy is quiet and non-invasive, and animals as well as people prefer a relaxing, comforting and refreshing treatment to having their bodies pricked with needles or invaded by drugs and operations. There are no chemical concoctions with as many side-effects as benefits! I have also found that energy therapy is effective for treating horse and rider together, so promoting the bond between the partnership.

The reason I say I have based my natural healing work upon Reiki is that purists would not call my work 'correct', either in the traditional or

Learning to use energy therapy can bring a new depth of communication between you and your horse.

westernised sense of the term. This is mainly because I include other forms of vibrational therapy and work on a very instinctive, intuitive level as opposed to following a regimented routine. However, I use the energy as I was taught, to draw it in and project it into the bodies of the horses and riders I work on. Usui himself based his healing work upon keeping the body in balance with proper diet, breathing, exercise and other factors. Perhaps, after all, my incorporation of bodywork of other kinds, vibrational medicine (the use of herbs, essential oils, meditation, visualisation and crystals) and other teaching methods with horses and riders would not be frowned upon by Usui! I also took counselling training, because people so often want to talk through their problems in a confidential and unconditional way. I felt that this was important because for me, working with energy is both a responsibility and a privilege, not simply a commercial activity or a business. It's all very well being able to give a treatment, but you have to be prepared for people to talk to you!

I also feel that it is important to teach others how to use energy for themselves. Usui taught that the training given to his students was simply a way to 'remind' them of how to draw in energy and use it to help others. As far as we know, there was no mention of treating animals with energy in Usui's time. For those of us working with energy today, however, some of our closest friends are animals.

Now that you know a little more about the background to energy as a healing therapy, we can move on to talk about how energy can be used to treat horse and rider.

Treatment Guidelines and Practice

Using energy therapy to treat horses and humans is very simple. Most people rely upon feel, instinct, intuition and how each body responds, to guide the way that they give a treatment. I use only my hands during a treatment and employ very few placements or hand positions. Ultimately, while it helps to give a problem area as direct a 'hit' of energy as possible, it is not necessary to have a rigorous, regimented approach to hand positions because the body will draw energy in as it needs it. A set of numerous hand positions is often taught for treating people, and some enjoy having a set routine to work through. I prefer to treat this as a framework and place my hands where I feel the energy is needed. Many practitioners use tools such as pendulums to dowse for energy imbalances in the body which may be causing physical problems. One of the main theories behind dowsing is that any tool used is simply there to amplify what the practitioner, at some level (often unconsciously) 'knows'. I prefer to work tool-free and to dowse or scan with my hands, to sense areas of imbalance by the way that the body pulls energy. Some people prefer the idea of using pendulums, as this feels more 'official' to them.

However you place your hands on the body, the idea is that you are projecting energy into the meridians and chakras. The chakras are a Hindu concept, the meridians a Chinese one; however, elements of both systems have been incorporated in Buddhism, which is where many energy therapies are thought to have originated. The idea of meridians, or energy pathways through the body, is well accepted and studied. Doctors also now feel that they are on the verge of definitive proof that the chakras exist, by measuring the source of the flow of energy from the bodies of those who work in the healing arts [1]. I, for one, feel happy to work with either chakras or meridians (particularly as the major chakras fall along the major meridians). Ultimately, it doesn't matter which you use as the basis for treatment – it's just important that it works!

Before commencing treatment with energy, it is important to bear in mind the question of ethics. No practitioner should make claims for miracles, simply that he or she gives a treatment if it is requested or required. It is also essential that you have permission to work with another individual's body. I always mentally ask permission of the horses that I treat, but on one level, it is possible that, by having 'encouraged' their owners to seek energy therapy, the horse has in fact asked for treatment! It is always worth remembering that, although you can offer energy therapy to anyone, each individual has the right to refuse, and to hold their disease or condition if they prefer – more of this later. It is also important that you offer energy with the individual's highest good in mind. It is my belief that even if one simply brings pleasure, comfort or an improvement in the quality of life to a human or horse, it's an advantage.

To simply treat a negative condition, someone who rides horses can be treated in exactly the same way as any other human – except that sometimes we're fitter! However, it can be of great benefit to treat horse and rider together. I have treated many riders for one-sidedness, stress, tension and obscure physical problems that have affected their horses. In this way, both horse and rider find a better way forward together. It is worth bearing this holistic relationship in mind when treating your own horse and learning to understand his behaviour. Here, I will give some guidelines, firstly for a basic treatment of a horse, then of a rider.

Treating horses with energy therapy

Making an assessment

If you're treating your own horse, a formal assessment is unnecessary, because you will know all the relevant details, so you can simply commence treatment with a quick scan of the body. When first approaching a horse you don't know, it is a good idea to make an assessment before commencing treatment. First, some basic information is required – name, age, type or breed and a brief outline of the problem (and diagnosis if available), as well as notes of any veterinary treatments which are currently being, or have previously been given. Next, the horse should be 'scanned' before treatment. Scanning performs two functions: to feel areas that pull in more energy through the hands than others, and need more healing; and to allow the horse to react by giving clues to where its pains or blockages are. If possible, it helps to gain a

When making an assessment of a horse for treatment, listen to the owner and observe the horse objectively.

connection or empathy with the horse, to establish its frame of mind; you can begin to learn how to do this simply by being aware of the horse's body language.

Always remember that in the UK it is an offence for anyone who is not a veterinary surgeon to make a medical diagnosis of an animal's condition. It is also the owner's responsibility to make sure that their veterinary surgeon is fully informed about any complementary therapies being given to their horse. Any practitioner giving therapy to a horse belonging to someone else should make sure that they have sufficient professional third-party liability insurance.

Scanning

Working with energy sensitises your hands to the feel of the body. By scanning the body with your hands, you learn to feel for areas that pull in more energy, or areas that have blockages. Keep your hand in the energy field a few inches from the body, and move your hand steadily down the body from the head to tail, and the upper body to the feet.

Scanning the horse's body with your hands can give you an insight into areas of imbalance.

Don't concentrate too hard, just relax and remain aware of any changes in the feeling in the palm of your hand and trust your instinctive feel, or intuition. You can re-scan the body after treatment to ensure that all areas have been treated sufficiently. Physicists are now examining the reality of information being received during the scanning process through transfer of energy. It is believed that communicating with the energy field of the body of another individual, horse or human, is a very basic transaction that takes place at a different level of awareness than we usually use in everyday life.

Signals to watch for

When making an assessment, it is worth bearing in mind that most horses are highly unlikely to have had this kind of therapy before, and so will not know what to expect. This is actually of benefit to the practitioner, because any reactions the horse has are genuine responses to the feeling of the energy flowing through the body. During the scanning process, horses may shuffle, twitch, stamp, move away from or into one's hands, swing their heads to touch a certain area – all of these are responses worth noting. For example, horses that repeatedly stamp one leg may pull in a vast amount of energy there during treatment, indicating that the area needs healing. I like to give horses plenty of scope for movement – but this can be difficult where horses have pain in the head. Because people feed titbits, it can be hard to tell a horse who wants a snack from one who is saying, 'It hurts, touch my head!'

Before treatment

Before commencing treatment, it is generally advisable to put a headcollar (US: halter) and rope on the horse. Drop the rope on the horse's neck so that it can be used to hold the horse if necessary; for example, to minimise any sudden displays of mutual grooming (which can be very forceful); to prevent biting or having your pockets searched for food. It is occasionally helpful for someone else to hold the horse or for the horse to be tied up.

Make sure you can work in peace with as little distraction as possible. Choose a suitable time of day for treatment, in other words, not while the horse is waiting to be fed or turned out.

Rugs should be removed and a soft bed provided for the horse to lie on if necessary.

A stable (stall) should be chosen which is out of view of too many visual distractions and out of strong wind or rain. In hot weather, make sure that there is shade and that both humans and equines are wearing plenty of insect repellent.

If people want to observe, they should remain as still and quiet as possible and not eat food – this can prove too distracting for the horse being treated.

Wear loose, comfortable clothing and make sure that you have on enough layers during winter. Clothing which rustles should be avoided, and your boots should have thick soles so that your feet don't become uncomfortable and break your concentration during treatment. Don't forget to take off your watch, as the energy can affect the way it works.

Always remember that energy therapy can never do harm but that, in cases of broken bones or open wounds, you should not begin to treat until the injury has been correctly set or stitched. Energy should always be applied from the sides of any major injury to encourage healing from within.

To give a treatment

The wonderful thing about using energy to treat a horse is that they have no preconceptions or objectivity; they can't pretend they don't feel it. Most horses enter a state of deep relaxation as the energy enters the body. Some horses take longer than others to reach this stage, and some may not feel comfortable enough to relax until the second treatment. Simply placing your hand on the horse and projecting energy in anywhere will help – however, it helps to have a set of hand positions to work through.

Begin treatment by placing your hand on the horse's near-side shoulder: this is fairly inoffensive and enables you to connect and start the flow of energy before beginning the treatment itself. As the horse begins to relax he will become still, drop his head slightly and begin to close his eyes. Dropping the bottom lip and moving the jaw is also a sign that the horse is accepting the energy and relaxing. He will begin to breathe deeply and gut sounds often increase. It can take some time to reach this stage if the horse is particularly nervous – in this case, take your time and be calm; this is no place for force. I have never treated a horse that did not settle enough to be still and accept treatment within around ten or, at the very most, fifteen minutes. Once this state is reached, the horse is highly unlikely to move very far. You can work with your hands directly on the surface of the horse's body, or slightly off it, within the energy field.

Once you have established contact, you can work through a series of hand positions as a framework, or just place your hands over areas that suggested themselves through scanning. You can treat specific problems simply by placing your hands either side of the area.

Hand positions

It is up to you to follow your instincts and listen to where your horse asks you to touch. Horses use many forms of body language to communicate where they would like your hands; they move around, twitch, swing the head and stamp – so be aware and let your horse guide you. Once the energy is flowing freely, relax and remain aware of the places where the pull on the energy is increased or decreased, or where your horse responds most strongly. Maintain contact at all times with at least one hand, to keep the flow of energy constant.

The hand position to aim for after the shoulder is found by sliding your hand along the neck to the head. This may take some patience with a head-shy horse. You are aiming to treat the energy centre at the crown of the head, located directly between the ears at the poll. This can have a profound effect on a horse and produce a deep sense of calm and relaxation. You should then aim to work on the forehead, and then back along the body stopping at the withers, loins, sacroiliac and base of the tail, all using your right hand. Your left hand can be used to treat the underside of the body at the same time, sliding along from the heart

HAND POSITIONS FOR TREATING HORSES

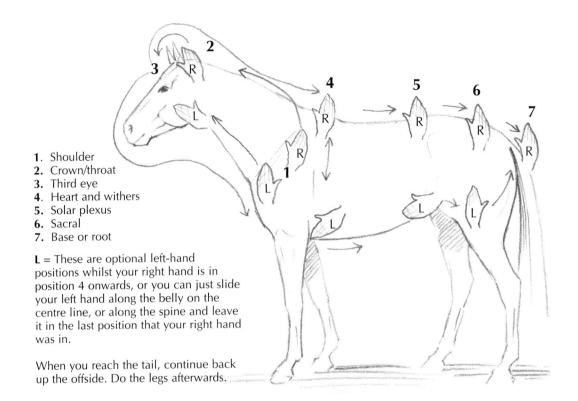

1. Shoulder
2. Crown/throat
3. Third eye
4. Heart and withers
5. Solar plexus
6. Sacral
7. Base or root

L = These are optional left-hand positions whilst your right hand is in position 4 onwards, or you can just slide your left hand along the belly on the centre line, or along the spine and leave it in the last position that your right hand was in.

When you reach the tail, continue back up the offside. Do the legs afterwards.

area, to the belly, and across the thigh to the base of the tail as you reach this with your right hand. This set of positions works along the major meridian on the top of the body, the 'governing vessel', and along the major stomach meridian and 'conception vessel' along the underside of the body. It also covers the locations of the seven main chakras.

Once you have reached the base of the tail, repeat the same positions right round to the off-side to the forehead, and finish at the shoulder. It is a good idea to then work down each of the legs separately, as too much standing and squatting during the treatment may serve to distract the horse.

How long you remain in each position is a matter of choice, how the energy feels, and being aware of the signals your horse gives. Generally, remaining in each position for a minimum of three minutes (on seven places each side) will bring you to a forty-minute treatment. A full treatment for a horse can take anything from forty to ninety minutes. However, treatments are not about watching the clock, but about using

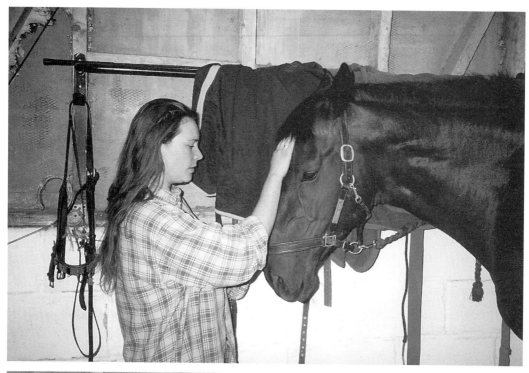

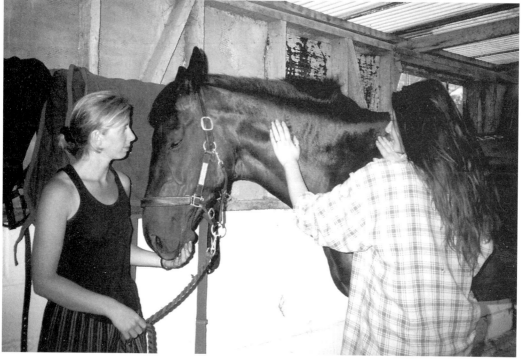

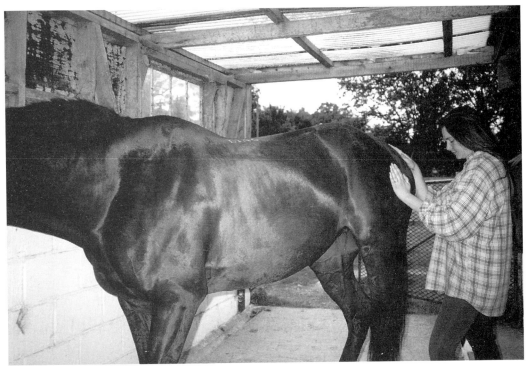

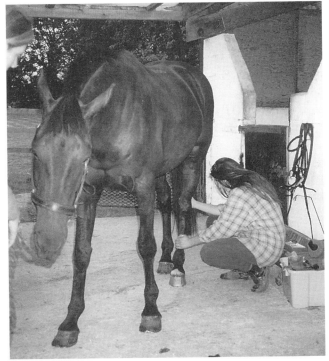

Giving a treatment. During the session, horses experience a deep state of relaxation which encourages the body to heal. This sequence shows a horse becoming still, quiet and relaxed through its treatment as I work from head to foot.

energy to encourage the body to heal, and this is more a matter for instinct. When scanning your horse, you may have found areas that pulled in significantly more energy than others, or felt cold and blocked. These are the places to concentrate on, and stay in until the flow of energy begins to subside or 'switch off'; this happens when the area has drawn in as much energy as it needs for the time being.

The horse's response during and after treatment

Some horses become so deeply relaxed during a treatment that they want to lie down. This doesn't happen often, but can occur during very strong treatments. Be aware that it is a possibility and make sure that you are in a safe area, ideally with adequate bedding. Horses who are about to lie down are usually in a very deep relaxed state; their legs begin to tremble and buckle slightly as they make a movement to kneel. I generally wait until they are comfortable and then continue treatment by squatting in a suitable position, where I am unlikely to be injured should the horse be startled into suddenly getting up.

Many horses undergo a number of releases during and after treatment. As well as yawning, the horse may stale, stretch, shake himself, or roll. During this process you may hear a pop or crack as tension is released (particularly through the neck and back). Wait for five or ten minutes after treatment, to make sure that the horse is waking up again, has adequate access to water and hay, and is warm and comfortable. The mouthing motions a horse makes during a treatment indicate the relief it can give – this kind of movement is not a conscious 'Oh, I think I'll lick my lips now' response, it's an automatic reaction to relaxation – like a sigh. Some people say it's a sign of submission, but it's more subtle and instinctive than that, and a horse undergoing a relaxing, soothing treatment hardly has anything to submit to. As I always say to sceptics – if you want to feel what your horse can feel, I'll give you a treatment too.

Treating people with energy therapy

Self-treatment

Self-treatment is a simple matter; you can simply place your hand wherever you want to on your body and project energy in. There is a set of guideline hand positions for a more complete self-treatment shown in

Chapter 8, in the section on self-healing. My favourite way to self-treat is simply to rest a hand on my knee, or when going to sleep at night, lay a hand on my stomach.

Making an assessment

If you don't know the person you're treating, it is a good idea to gather some basic information: name, age and a brief history of the problem, a diagnosis if there is one, as well as any kind of medical treatments that have been or are currently being given. With people, this can take some time as a large part of the release process is in talking about long-held physical pains, habits or emotional issues. Then, make the person comfortable in whatever position they are going to remain for the session. Finally, scan the body with your hands from head to foot before you begin the treatment.

Before commencing treatment

How you organise the practicalities of a treatment will depend entirely upon the situation and place you are working in. Treatments can be given sitting in a chair, on a sofa, a bed, on a blanket on the ground in the middle of a field in the sunshine, or on a purpose-designed treatment couch. I have given treatments in stables (barns), pubs, car parks, market places, shops, in the street, at equestrian competitions, in clients' houses, in healing centres and at my own home. The more relaxed you are about what you are doing, the less you will find that places are important. When treating people in their own homes, it helps to have a portable couch which you can take with you and set up; it saves a lot of difficulty trying to find a comfortable position to work in. The most important point is that both you and the person you are treating are comfortable.

Privacy is often very important to someone who is allowing you to work on his or her body. Make sure that you ask if they have any part of the body that they prefer you don't touch, and if so, work above that area, not on it.

Unless you are working in public, most people prefer the privacy of a closed, quiet room where you will not be disturbed or distracted by noise. Turn off or unplug the telephone.

Soft lighting, gentle, relaxing music, burning incense or essential oils and making sure that the temperature is right for both of you all help to produce a relaxing atmosphere.

It is up to the person being treated to decide what they wear; loose,

HAND POSITIONS FOR A SEATED TREATMENT

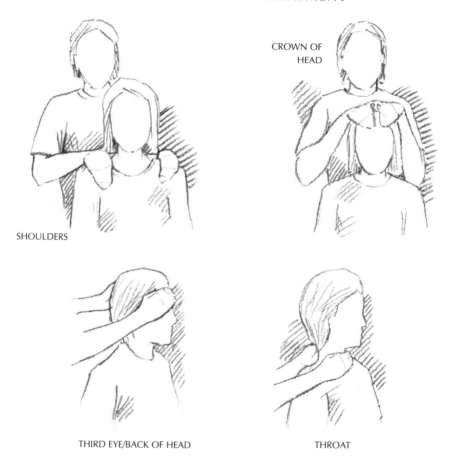

CROWN OF HEAD

SHOULDERS

THIRD EYE/BACK OF HEAD

THROAT

comfortable clothing is best. Some people prefer to be covered by a sheet or blanket (which you will work above). Provide pillows for under the head, back or knees as necessary for anyone who needs them.

Wash your hands first and be aware of your own personal hygiene – no garlic the night before!

Wear loose, comfortable clothing yourself and, as with treating horses, clothing which rustles should be avoided. Ideally you should remove your shoes as well as your watch. Ask the person you are treating to remove their watch and hearing aid, if they wear one. Check if they have a pacemaker as this may be adversely affected by the energy.

Again, though energy therapy can do no harm, in cases of broken bones or open wounds, you should not begin to treat until the injury has been correctly set or stitched. Energy should always be applied from the sides of any injury to encourage healing from within.

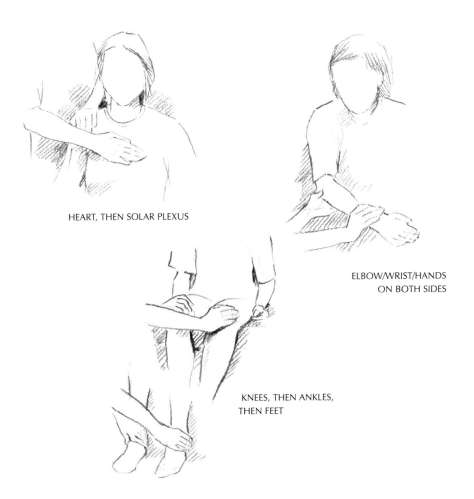

HEART, THEN SOLAR PLEXUS

ELBOW/WRIST/HANDS
ON BOTH SIDES

KNEES, THEN ANKLES,
THEN FEET

To give a treatment

Begin by connecting with the person's shoulders. This helps to establish
a flow of energy before moving to the head. Then, you can work
through the set of hand positions given according to how the person is
positioned. I do not agree with turning over a patient who is lying
down, as it is so disruptive. Again, use the hand positions as a
framework but place your hands wherever you feel areas of imbalance
in the body. I like to work from the head down to the feet, then up again
the other side. Many practitioners finish at the feet, believing that this
leaves the energy grounded; I prefer to make sure that I have worked
right around the body and that finishing at the head leaves the energy
topped-up!

HAND POSITIONS FOR A RECUMBENT TREATMENT

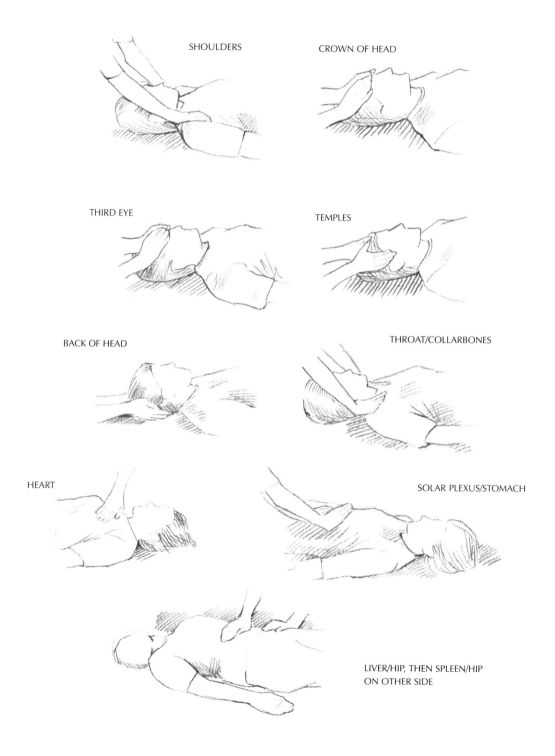

SHOULDERS

CROWN OF HEAD

THIRD EYE

TEMPLES

BACK OF HEAD

THROAT/COLLARBONES

HEART

SOLAR PLEXUS/STOMACH

LIVER/HIP, THEN SPLEEN/HIP
ON OTHER SIDE

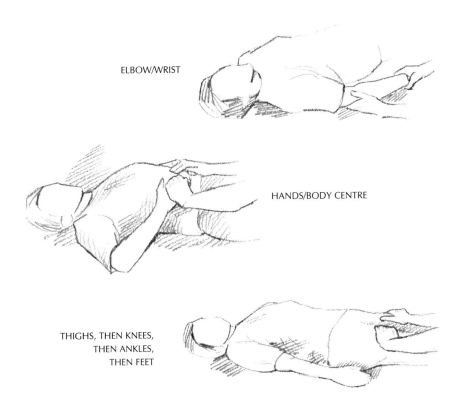

ELBOW/WRIST

HANDS/BODY CENTRE

THIGHS, THEN KNEES,
THEN ANKLES,
THEN FEET

A full treatment for a person will take around an hour; holding each of the 'standard' hand positions for around three minutes will take you to this time. However, treatment is more a matter for instinct and I tend to wait until the flow into each area has subsided before moving. Where there are blockages, this may take substantially longer than three minutes. Some people like you to concentrate on the area which is an issue. When I finish a treatment, I always make a sweeping motion down the length of the body with my hands within the energy field, to 'smooth down' the energy. I also shake, blow, or rinse my hands to cool the flow of energy and mentally 'disconnect' myself from the other person.

During treatment

Under treatment, the body generally reaches a state of deep relaxation. Most people close their eyes and remain extremely quiet, sometimes even dropping off to sleep. Sometimes, as part of the release process, people cry or talk. Often they will yawn and gut sounds will increase.

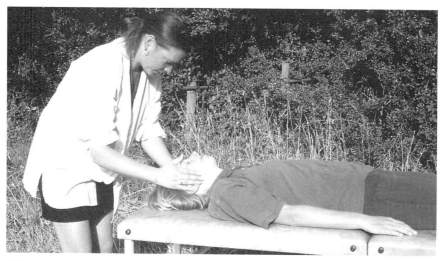

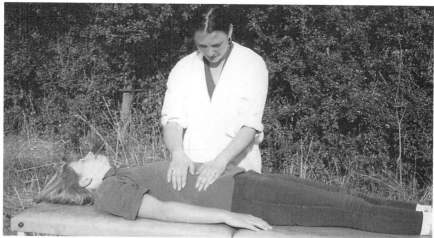

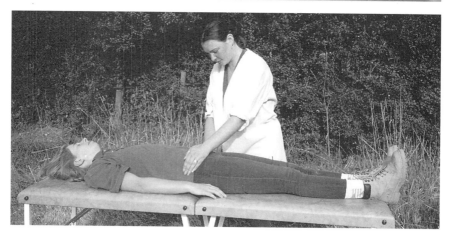

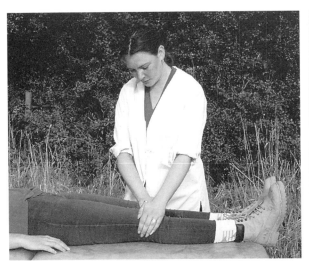

This sequence shows a treatment being given to a rider. It is not strictly necessary to have a complex set of hand positions – simply place your hands where you feel the body needs treatment.

Most importantly during treatment, keep your own body movements smooth and fluid; move between hand positions without breaking contact, always placing your following hand over the position of your leading one before moving. This helps to reduce the element of surprise as you move between one position and another, as well as keeping the flow of energy constant. Most importantly, keep your touch light and don't lean on your clients or breathe over them.

Points to remember

- The hand positions given are simply a framework – not a regulation. If you want to place your hands differently, follow your intuition.
- Do not apply energy to a broken bone until it has been set, and then only give it from either side, not directly above the break. Energy can be given to the person in another part of their body to help deal with shock or pain. Wounds, breaks and burns should always be treated from the sides rather than directly above. Always use your common sense and first-aid in an emergency.
- If the person you are treating prefers not to be touched in certain places, it is best to work above them, within the energy field. You can give a full treatment within an inch or a few inches of the body, and some people respond more strongly to the energy being given on this level than directly to the surface of their physical body. Energy given

HAND POSITIONS FOR TREATING BACKS

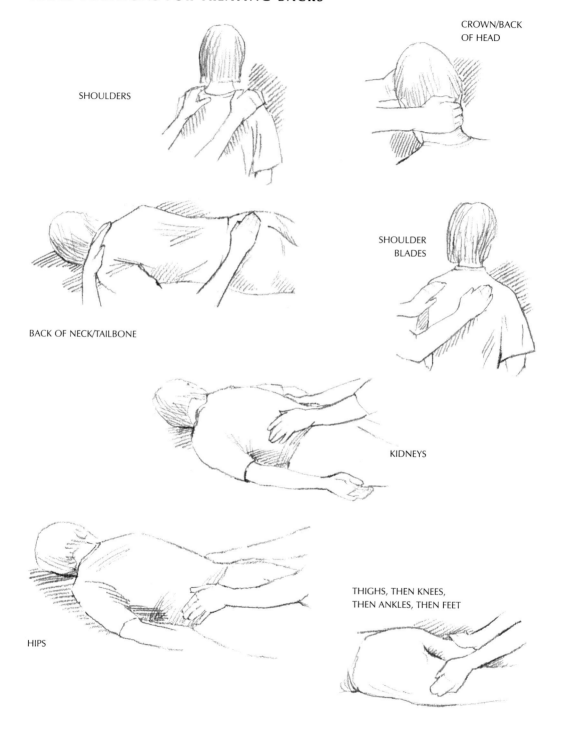

CROWN/BACK
OF HEAD

SHOULDERS

SHOULDER
BLADES

BACK OF NECK/TAILBONE

KIDNEYS

HIPS

THIGHS, THEN KNEES,
THEN ANKLES, THEN FEET

directly within the energy field also helps to prevent a physical condition from manifesting.

After treatment

After treatment, allow the person to sit quietly for a while to 'ground' after the feeling of being 'spaced out' that treatments can induce. Offer a drink and make sure that tissues are available for anyone who cries, as well as a toilet for anyone who needs it.

One of the main releases that people undergo is the process of talking about what they felt during treatment. It is important to be able to listen unconditionally and with empathy. It is also important that you do not try to offer your opinion or personal advice about their condition or situation.

Sometimes, during a treatment, you may gain insight into the condition that you are treating. This may be purely due to body language, cellular electrical signals, the more abstract concept of a collective consciousness, or working closely within the energy field of another individual. This applies to both horses and humans, but I would hesitate to claim that this kind of communication means that you are being 'talked to' by a horse. You may become aware of the cause of the illness or memory-scar and the problems connected to it. You may also find ideas popping into your head, quite aside from your conscious thoughts, about what can be done to help facilitate recovery and healing. It is wise to pass this information on to a client only if you genuinely feel it appropriate to do so. It is vital that you do this uncon-ditionally, without bringing in any judgement of your own.

You should maintain a great respect for the individual you treat, as well as the process of treatment. As you work with energy, you will become more aware of the areas of the physical body and conditions that are related to emotional issues. Always put yourself in the place of the person you are treating and choose your words carefully. The emotional causes of physical disease also apply, though in more basic terms, to horses.

Energy in context

The simple procedures given here for a **basic** treatment form the **basis** of working with your horse, or other people. Many of you will be happy to use energy therapy in such a straightforward way. However, you can also treat horses and riders together, and use energy to relax and calm a horse if it has a specific problem, for example, if it dislikes being rugged up. This is how I use healing energy therapy – in a practical way as part of an holistic approach to healing. Much of my work with horses and riders involves not just the straight treatment, but incorporating it with bodywork, physical training for horses and riders, and all kinds of vibrational medicine. In the next chapter, I will explain some of my methods and how you can use energy to treat all kinds of conditions in your own horse, and in a wide variety of situations, as well as the influence of your horse's mind on the health of his body.

The Dynamics of Healing Horses

Long-term health

Energy therapy is such a simple, natural and powerful way of healing that it can be used in the most basic of forms, as a stand-alone therapy. Although all kinds of problems can be healed in both mind and body, it is important to address the long-term well-being of your horse. In other words, it's all very well re-balancing the energy of the body, but if the body persistently needs to be re-balanced, it is a better idea to address the factors causing the imbalance. The ideal is to maintain and improve well-being on a progressive, lifelong basis, as opposed simply to using energy to cope with problems as they occur. Minds and bodies change every day, and life never ceases to create situations to which horses react. Practitioners of energy therapy are concerned with the aim of long-term well-being in the face of the 'stuff' that life creates when they talk about releasing a problem for good, as opposed simply to clearing up the symptoms. With this aim in mind, it can be helpful to include other kinds of work alongside energy therapy, as part of your horse's health-care regime.

I feel that one sensible approach is to incorporate energy therapy as part of a whole-system healing for horses and riders. This fits in with the original system of natural healing taught by Mikao Usui. His work was based on Eastern medicine, involving use of the 'five elements' – water, metal, earth, fire and wood (the elements do vary according to the system used) – to keep mind and body in balance, through nutrition, mental approach and exercise. Although the concept of the use of elements is alien to most Westerners, the basic idea is that of working to heal both mind and body continually in terms of nourishment, physical exercise and mental well-being. You can't expect to maintain your horse's health with energy therapy if he's not being properly fed!

If you are working closely with your own horse, it is possible to monitor changes and improvements as they occur, and gradually to bring in new factors or holistic treatments as part of the healing process. It is wise to introduce each new element slowly, and to wait for a reaction before changing or adding another – if you use too many at once, you have no way of telling what is having a beneficial effect on your horse's health.

Because energy therapy is so natural, it can also be used alongside any other treatment or medication, traditional or otherwise, and can improve the effectiveness of other therapies. Healing with energy has been used to help improve the results of medical treatment, to reduce side-effects, speed up healing time, help to eliminate pain and lower stress, so you can even use it to help your horse through a course of conventional treatment or an operation.

What can energy therapy treat in horses?

Energy is both powerful and gentle. In use therapeutically throughout the world, it is said to have aided in healing almost every known illness and injury. Everything benefits from receiving some energy. Without citing too long a list, I have found energy therapy beneficial for healing all kinds of physical conditions in horses. I have treated pulled tendons, muscles and ligaments, bruising, broken bones, splints, severe wounds, colds, colic, hormonal imbalances, back problems and spine curvature, all kinds of locomotive issues, joint problems such as arthritis and degenerative joint disease, sores, infections, asthma, fatigue and all manner of obscure conditions. Whatever your horse is suffering from, you can give him treatments on a regular basis to help heal his body.

There are many conditions that appear to be physical problems, but in fact turn out to be emotional in origin. There is a very fine line between physical and emotional, or memory-scar issues, in horses – head-shaking, for example, can be caused through allergy, injury or through nervous tension. Energy therapy can be most beneficial in encouraging a horse to relax and clear the old, useless memories which are simply creating fear. I have treated horses who spook, are nervous, stressed or tense; who bite, kick, bolt, box-walk; who panic, are sour, overworked, withdrawn, aggressive ... once again, the list is endless. Again, whatever your horse's issue, you can give him basic treatments regularly to help clear his problem. Where treatments can have the most profound effect is in helping horses who have behavioural patterns that their owners simply don't understand – where horses have suddenly started 'doing something'. If you are a fairly open individual you may find that working with energy serves to increase your sensitivity to, and awareness of, such issues.

Physical healing for horses

I believe that the intention behind healing with energy is the most vital element of treatment. You should treat your horse in an unconditional way, to help to bring the body back into balance. Working unconditionally means that, no matter what the diagnosis, you offer energy to the body, without a fixed aim or end-result in mind, for the horse's highest good. This way of thinking isn't quite in line with many traditional approaches, which will give up on conditions that are considered incurable. In other words, although you may know that the horse has arthritis, you don't give up, and you don't offer healing with the express aim that his arthritis is cured. Your intent should be simply that the energy works to heal for the animal's highest good. Bear in mind that any outward problem may have other contributory factors that you are not aware of – particularly if you treat a horse that you don't know.

Sometimes, using energy on the body will help to give clues to the factors behind a presenting problem. However, it is not the aim of an holistic or complementary therapist to diagnose, and it is illegal to do so. The main aim is to bring the body back to health, whatever the problem or symptoms. It sounds like a contradiction in terms to say that energy therapy can release the root causes of issues, and then to say that a diagnosis is not necessary. However, if you consider that many horses who are lame have a back problem, and vice versa, it is often the case that one problem has gone unnoticed due to treatment for the other.

In cases such as these, energy therapy can work to heal and release the problem whether it has been identified or not, and can help to trace the source of the imbalance. I have seen lameness that was pronounced 'incurable' because the leg has been treated in isolation, where the pain was due to an unnoticed problem in the back, caused by the saddle and being made worse by the rider. I have treated another lameness that was traced to a problem in the neck; in this case, scanning the energy flow of the body allowed me to find and treat this issue, where conventional methods, working on a purely symptomatic basis on the leg, had given up. I have even treated an habitual lameness, where the body had learned to carry itself in a certain way due to fear of pain and muscle wastage. Although it is not strictly necessary to know about these factors (except where the problem is being caused by an outside influence such as a saddle or riding), scanning your horse's body can naturally lead to finding the area of the body that is out of balance. This is why working unconditionally and with an open mind is important – you might find that your own horse's condition is not what it had first seemed to be.

Therapy for behavioural work

Horses readily accept energy therapy, primarily because it is physical and involves touch – part of the horse's natural way of communicating. This is of particular value for behavioural work. There are two distinct areas of treatment for behavioural problems – the first is simply for relaxing and calming the horse. This is helpful in working with nervous horses, for example; or during potentially stressful situations, such as when clipping a young horse for the first time. The second distinct area of application is when treating the horse for a remedial behavioural problem. This involves combining treatments with the handling or ridden issue that the horse most fears – allowing it to release the old, negative behaviour.

'Memory-scarring' is where the memory of a traumatic event or physical pain has resulted in a related behavioural pattern, which has become a habit in the absence of the original stimulus. This kind of obscure problem is often where energy therapy can be most beneficial, in encouraging a horse to relax and clear the old, useless memories, which are simply creating fear. In spite of so many advances in behavioural work with horses, there are still very few establishments which would not employ the use of restraint or force to 'school' or train a horse through this kind of issue. When working with energy, however, it's quite a different story.

Healing behaviour with energy

It is now becoming widely accepted throughout the West that it is difficult to separate physical illness from state of mind, and many medical doctors agree that illnesses are related to a patient's emotional condition. By becoming aware of the connection between a physical disease and the underlying emotional issue, that issue can be addressed; conversely, because energy clears negativity, emotional issues are healed, minimising and healing the physical problems manifested. In human patients, this works beautifully because people can talk through their emotional issues, helping to clear and release them. But how can we facilitate behavioural healing with horses, who can't talk?

The first step is to become aware of the ways in which your horse communicates with you. As most humans would find it hard to replicate the vocal sounds that horses make, the easiest way for us to understand horses is through their body language. This forms a large part of their communication with each other, and provides a key for us in understanding what they are trying to tell us. You can work to heal your own

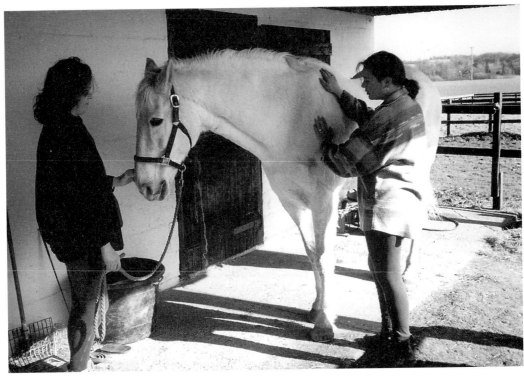

The first touch on the shoulder can be a powerful moment and, for this horse, comes as a welcome relief.

horse's behavioural issues using the same principles as in humans – but by communicating with physical actions rather than vocal words. Instead of communicating by voice – 'It's OK, everything will be fine, don't worry' – you can communicate physically by showing your horse with your actions that it is OK, and this doesn't hurt, and things are fine. Behavioural conditions also benefit from the introduction and use of herbs with calming and sedative properties, or essential oils, which help to maintain stability and dispel fear. Bach Flower Remedies can also be of great benefit in releasing and dispelling 'emotional' negativity.

Listening to your horse

Our horses are communicating with us all the time, but their behaviour only tends to become glaringly obvious when there is a problem. This tends to be because we can't understand why the horse is doing what he's doing – in other words, what he is trying to communicate. People say, 'He's just started doing this for no reason.' That's like saying that, for example, you have come home from work in a bad mood for 'no reason'! The reason is always present; it's just a question of finding out what it is. Horses are showing us what's wrong – but because of the language barrier, we sometimes have difficulty in understanding them.

Let's follow this analogy a little further. Perhaps you came home from work in a bad mood because you'd had a terrible day. Your boss had been nagging you, and you were getting to the point where you had had enough and were considering looking for another job, away from the problems. No wonder you're feeling grumpy. Now, what about your horse who, for 'no apparent reason', hides at the back of the stable (stall) whenever someone walks past with a saddle? Maybe his saddle doesn't fit too well and, in spite of doing his best to tolerate the pain, he is beginning to get really sore. Actually, his behaviour is quite logical. He has begun to associate having to wear a saddle with pain and is, quite sensibly, trying to avoid it.

But, you're saying, if I buy my horse a new saddle, surely he should stop behaving that way? Think about your bad day at work. Your boss is a pain, so you try to avoid him – you carry the memory of your experiences with you and change your behaviour accordingly. Your horse reacts the same way – carrying the memory and trying to avoid the situation. He sees someone approach with a saddle, and instinctively associates it with pain; he can't know that it's a new saddle that fits. His back needs to heal and he needs to be shown that whenever someone comes to his stable (stall), it won't hurt; in the same way as you need to learn by experience that your boss can be far more pleasant when he's not so stressed. Of course, this is a somewhat over-humanised example, but this kind of analogy can help to unravel the process behind equine behaviour that may at first appear obscure. An important point to make is that if you view the situation the other way round – that the horse is still instinctively reacting in the absence of the pain – this can help to shed light on human behaviour, and how people instinctively react through memory-scarring.

The root of the problem – and releasing it

Therefore, when faced with a problem that might first appear obscure, energy therapy can help on a number of levels. Perhaps nobody knows that your horse's back is sore because there are no obvious marks – he has just started hiding from people. By scanning his body, it is possible to feel the areas that pull in a greater amount of energy than others – in this case, the injured area under the saddle would greatly increase the pull and you would be aware of the change. Secondly, offering energy to your horse's body can help to relieve his physical pain through facilitating healing. Thirdly, you can heal his behaviour through using energy to relax him in conjunction with physical handling work.

It is not enough simply to change your saddle, as your horse will have come to associate the saddle with punishment – through constant reinforcement of the pain. So you can treat your horse so that his physical pain heals. Then you can use energy to relax him as you gradually re-introduce the saddle, to help him to remain calm in spite of his fears. As he gradually learns to stay relaxed and peaceful in the face of the thing that most threatened him, he releases all his old fears and tension and learns to trust again. This is a good example of the kind of problem that lots of riders just live with ('oh, he's a bit cold-backed'); or, having fitted a new saddle, try to overlay by retraining.

Working on the head can produce some of the most powerful releases and a deep moment of togetherness.

USES FOR ENERGY THERAPY IN BEHAVIOURAL WORK

To calm and relax
- Nerves
- Spooking
- Tension, causing handling/riding difficulties
- Lack of confidence
- After a shock, injury or accident, or foaling
- During weaning or separation
- After a move
- Before and after competitions
- As a treat during grooming

As a preventive measure
- For clipping
- When loading
- When first breaking to ride, wearing a saddle and carrying a rider
- When introducing to traffic
- When first shoeing

For clearing remedial problems
- Kicking
- Biting
- Head-shaking
- Jogging/jigging
- Aggression
- Barging and rushing
- Bolting
- Rearing and nappiness
- Fear of specific things – saddles, rugs, traffic, jumping, noise, dogs, etc.

Healing a horse's mind

On a mental level, energy therapy promotes confidence and calm, and is of benefit for nervous behaviour, tension, anxiety and all manner of behavioural problems. In terms of the behavioural reactions to, and causes of physical problems, there is generally not the same complexity of factors to be considered with such an instinctive animal as the horse as there is with a human being. Horses' physical injuries are very often the result of accidents, or are caused by situations engineered by their riders, for example over-riding or poor riding.

However, there are certain horse personality types that are predisposed to physical symptoms or disease. Horses who are easily excitable, always rushing everywhere and prone to spooking or panicking are often the ones who suffer accidents through skidding round corners in the field or sliding about on the road, and falling over. The resultant injuries might range from over-extension of joints and muscles, to impact injuries from collisions with either the ground or an object. In such cases, it is extremely beneficial to treat the emotional or temperamental condition behind the physical problem to help reduce the likelihood of such situations in future. Another case is that of horses who are good at putting up with pain and working in spite of it. Such characters are prone to over-use by inconsiderate riders and handlers – or just because we don't know there's a problem until it's too late. These horses can be the first to suffer from joint problems due to sheer over-use at an early age. Broadly speaking, the behavioural causes behind these conditions are not complicated, but are certainly worth considering and addressing.

When energy therapy can help

When considering what you can use energy therapy to treat in a mental or behavioural context, you can see that the conditions you can help to relieve and release are as many and varied as horses themselves. Energy therapy can be used as a stand-alone treatment to relax and calm nervous, spooky, tense or stressed horses. It can be used in a calming or relaxing way as a preventive measure, for example, when loading a young horse for the first time and during the breaking-in process. It can also be used as part of the handling and training process, where horses have remedial problems that need to be released and retrained. For example, if you have a horse who is terrified of rugs; you can begin giving the horse energy therapy before putting the rug on, and you will find that the horse remains calm and learns to let go of his anxiety over the problem. This is the kind of issue that many trainers would tackle simply through de-sensitising, which sometimes has to be repeated again at a later date.

You can use energy to calm a horse in any tense situation, for example, when leading, before or during competition, weaning, box-rest, and so on. It also gives a wonderful added treat during grooming.

The chart opposite gives some examples of how energy can be used in each context.

All horses respond to treatment. This tough little pony thoroughly enjoys her session.

Total health

As mentioned earlier, there are many horse problems which you can treat purely through giving energy alone. However, because of the importance of treating the body as a whole, in some circumstances it can be helpful to introduce other vibrational therapies to aid the long-term rehabilitation of the horse involved. As you get to know the individual you are working on (especially if it's your own horse), you can learn a little more about factors influencing the problem and you may gradually introduce additional elements, such as a change of diet or using homeopathic remedies, to assist in alleviating the condition. This applies where, for example, a nutritional factor was involved in exacerbating the presenting problem.

I consider the use of herbs as part of the diet to be of great importance in rehabilitating all kind of physical problems. My feelings are based upon the fact that, in the past, horses would have had access to the kind of pasture where an abundance of herbs of all kinds grew and where they could eat whatever they felt they needed. This is a little like the idea of catering to our own body's cravings for food, which may be the result of dietary requirements. For example, when treating a horse with a degenerative or arthritic joint condition, aside from using energy therapy, I sometimes feed herbs with beneficial properties to help treat the arthritis. Healing with energy and feeding herbs can be combined with a practical management system that suits the horse in terms of combining rest and exercise (including physical therapy) with a suitable diet. If it is indicated, for example if the horse is stressed by pain, a blend of calming and relaxing essential oils can be used, particularly at night where horses are generally unsupervised and unhandled for a long period of time. The use of a homeopathic remedy may be appropriate, or a crystal to aid in the healing process, but remember these are still just 'medicines' for 'symptoms'.

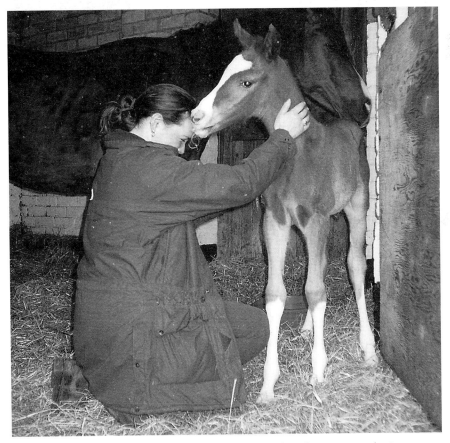

This three-day-old foal is welcomed into the world with some comforting energy therapy – a great way to encourage bonding with humans.

Muscle-testing (kinesiology) to show clients areas of imbalance in their own horse's body. This process can be deeply convincing for sceptics, who are used as surrogates for testing their own horses.

Vibration and intent

I am a great believer in vibrational medicines of all kinds, mainly due to the beneficial effects that I have seen through using them. I am sure that, in fact, there is far more to be discovered in this area. For example, homeopathy still holds secrets – e.g. the remedy being deactivated through touch, and becoming more potent as it is diluted furthermore. Is it possible, perhaps, that the deactivation occurs because the remedy is on the right vibrational frequency for the body and that it has already been absorbed? Is it possible, as with crystals, and in Dr Bach's exploratory work with his flower remedies, and with energy therapy, that the body only has to come into contact with the remedy on the right vibrational frequency for the condition being treated, for it to work?

The idea that the therapeutic properties of herbs and stones can be absorbed on contact with the body is not a new one. Ancient cultures used amulets that were thought to bestow on the wearer the properties contained within the amulet. Amulets can be seen decorating not just people, but horses and other animals, in ancient etchings and pictures, and have been found among the burial goods inside graves the world over. They are still made by many cultures, from stones, teeth, feathers, coloured ribbons, herbs, bones, etc. For example, a horse going into battle might wear an amulet for protection. This could be made from the tooth of a wolf or bear for bravery; a sprig of oak or thyme for courage; and a tiger's-eye stone for confidence, clear thought and willpower; all hung on, or wrapped in, a red ribbon for strength and energy. Perhaps the practice of wearing amulets slowly degenerated, as knowledge was lost, into colourful decoration of browbands and rosettes.

The use of 'ingredients' in this almost magical way is the principle behind all kinds of medicine, Eastern and Western – the use of naturally occurring ingredients that can provide the properties needed in a remedy. It also forms the principle behind the 'spells' cast by witches – again, the whole issue is that of intent. If one accepts the idea that projection of energy is possible at all, then it may be perfectly possible to attach or send energy to a physical object or ritual as a demonstration of intent; be it healing or any other aim.

Healing horse, healing rider

To summarise, energy can be used to treat not just physical problems (like back pain) in both horse and rider, but emotional issues (like fear), and conditions where it is not so easy to make a distinction. It is

Releasing tension as horse and rider work together.

important that the horse and rider are not treated as two separate entities in isolation, but as a whole. Because of the close, almost symbiotic nature of the relationship between horse and rider, it is impossible to treat a horse's problems without considering its environment and the actions of its handler. If a horse 'starts doing something', this has an effect on the rider – if the rider 'starts doing something', this may have triggered a problem for the horse – and the problem is compounded as the downward spiral begins. In this way, once the healing process begins, it has the same effect but in an upward spiral – once the horse has started to improve, the rider becomes less stressed and happier with the horse; and the horse becomes less stressed and happier with the rider.

This is how horse and rider can find a better way forward together. It is worth bearing this holistic relationship in mind when treating your own horse and learning to understand his behaviour. Is it something he has started doing of his own accord, or does his behaviour involve a trigger from you? In the next chapter, we will examine the dynamics of healing for riders.

Healing for Riders – Balancing the Whole Person

Energy therapy and you

Much of what I have said in relation to working to heal horses' physical ailments applies to working with people. Energy can be used alongside any other therapy or treatment, orthodox or otherwise; it can never do harm and always, at some level, benefits the recipient. Healing with energy can often be highly effective when used alone to treat people, due to the inextricable link between emotional and physical conditions. Because of the process of talking and thought that goes with almost any action the human body makes, the release process that takes place with healing is often a matter of both treatment and talking, naturally rather than by design. If you're self-treating, it can help to have someone that you can discuss your own condition or issues with. The great advantage to self-treatment, though, is that nobody else has to be involved – you can work on your own body any time, any place, anywhere.

With the aim of addressing the long-term total health of the human mind and body, the healing process can be a powerful and significant move forward for many people. Many riders come to complementary therapists because they have a recurring problem, pain or condition that has not been eased through conventional methods, or where nothing can actually be found 'wrong' using standard diagnostics. I have worked with countless cases where, in spite of visiting all kinds of therapists and trainers, people have become locked in a cycle of relapse and recovery. It is because of this that, in order to effect a long-term relief, I feel it so important to work to heal the whole system on an ongoing basis. In other words, to maintain and improve the individual continually in terms of nourishment, physical exercise and mental well-being.

Horse and rider: a symbiosis

Because of the strength and influence of the relationship between horse and rider, horses presented for treatment are often swiftly followed into healing energy therapy by their riders. This is partly because riders see the benefits and relaxation imparted by treatments with energy therapy upon their horses, and want to feel the effect for themselves. It is also partly because, in very many cases, it is impossible to extract the problems of horse and rider from each other and work on them in isolation, and it is not beneficial to try!

It is sadly true that many of the problems horses have are caused by their riders; perhaps because, ultimately, horses were not exactly designed to do a lot of what we ask them to do. However, as we all keep horses for our own reasons and want to ride them, most of us wish to continue to improve our relationships with them, and to enhance our enjoyment of life together. Most riders are enlightened and brave enough to genuinely want to work to achieve real progress, and to get out of the situation they're stuck in.

Some riders want to work with energy not because they have a problem, but simply to improve the way that they work with their own horses, at home or in competition. Both horses and riders benefit from treatment together where a problem has become embedded and new ways need to be learned. Many riders admit that they become tense and stressed by some of the behaviour their horses exhibit, and that their horses pick up that tension only too quickly. This is when a partnership can so easily start on the downward spiral where stress exacerbates a problem, causing more stress, and so on.

It is also true that many people buy or choose animals that, in many ways, mirror their own personalities, or that their horses begin to mirror the personalities of their riders through handling. For example, tense riders often produce tense horses; very laid-back riders tend to have a soporific effect upon the horses they ride and handle. Because of this, the same treatments and remedies can often work as powerfully for both horse and rider. It can be a liberating and enjoyable process for riders to be treated alongside their horses, as people see the way that their animals respond to the same treatments they are having.

Many riders benefit from energy therapy very early in treatment, because it can 'recharge their batteries' so quickly. Such a boost can provide the energy and willpower to work through the situation.

People often say, 'You must think I'm a terrible rider,' or 'You must think my horse is awful.' This happens generally where people are working in isolation and don't have a measure of normality by which to gauge their own issues. Most of us have been guilty of intellectualising to such an extent that a problem becomes blown out of all proportion. (I often say that horses and other animals are far less complicated to work on than humans – people say, why, when they can't talk, and tell you what's wrong? Well, animals don't have the intellectual issues behind rehabilitation that people do. People are so much more complex!) It's wonderful to see the relief on somebody's face when you tell them that, in fact, you see problems far worse than theirs on a regular basis; that of course, there's hope! The happier, more relaxed rider makes for a happier, more relaxed horse and so the pair make their first steps on the road to recovery.

Working with energy on the human body

People usually feel energy therapy as a tingling, flowing feeling; generally warm or hot. It is a great treatment for sceptics because you don't have to believe in it for it to work – it just does. The energy imparts a sense of profound relaxation and well-being, and some people have treatments purely as a relaxing treat. Therapy works to boost energy levels and inner strength, promotes health and well-being, and raises awareness. This increase in awareness is of enormous benefit in gaining a deeper connection with our horses, particularly for those of you who compete with your horse.

On a physical level, I have used energy therapy to treat a whole variety of ailments. These include cuts, bruises, broken bones, back problems, aching joints; muscle, tendon and ligament injuries; wounds, headaches, coughs, colds, flu, malaria, infections, bronchitis, toothache, fatigue, eczema, kidney problems; serious long-term illness such as cancer; obscure conditions such as muscular imbalance; insomnia, PMS...you name it! As always, there is a blurring of distinction between purely physical problems and those of emotional origin and vice versa. On an emotional or spiritual level, energy therapy is extremely effective in promoting a sense of peace and well-being that enables you to face life in a relaxed and confident way. I have used it to treat nerves, fear, panic attacks, tension, stress, depression and during times of upheaval, such as relationship break-ups or major life changes.

A fresh approach

Much of the time, riders presenting with a physical problem will have a name for it, or a diagnosis from a medic. I have found that this can actually be limiting in terms of recovery. If someone tells you that your condition is incurable, the impact this has on your mind is considerable. Labelling someone as 'stressed' or 'depressive' hardly creates a feeling of encouragement and positive thought. Scanning the body for energy blockages and imbalances can lead to the detection of areas that need treatment, and to finding areas that may not have been treated before. Sometimes, this enables us to throw out the old label for a condition, or to trace it to a different area of the body. The use of applied kinesiology (or muscle-testing, as it is sometimes known), can be valuable as a diagnostic tool, as well as to find new ways of approaching treatment. The laws are far less strict for complementary practitioners treating people than they are for animals – people are considered to be able to make their own choices, in terms of treatment, and about what they call their conditions.

Regardless of the presenting problem, it is always important to give energy unconditionally and with the intent of healing the individual for their highest good, even if you're treating yourself. Don't let diagnoses limit your way of thinking; 'incurable' to one practitioner simply means they can't help using their own methods, not that nobody else, anywhere on the planet, will ever be able to help. It is therefore essential that energy is offered unencumbered by specifics. In other words, it is as well not to ask for your back pain to be cured, but that the energy works to heal as it is best for the body receiving it. At an early stage, even if you are treating yourself, it is always possible that there are contributory factors about which you know nothing, or indeed, may never know anything. If a condition is to be healed, the whole condition must be healed and not just the symptoms.

Energy to ride

Where somebody has presented for treatment with a riding issue – for example, tension, postural problems, a recurring pain, one-sidedness, or as part of the 'big picture' of a 'resistant' horse, for example – it is essential to work with the rider mounted, as well as unmounted. Mounted work can quickly and powerfully release pain and long-held injuries and habits within the body. This process can give riders a startling insight into how it can feel to work with their horses in a new way. In turn, this can dramatically influence the horse's way of going. This gives both rider and horse the opportunity to act and react in new ways which, in turn, can soon become new habits as the old ones are released.

Sometimes when a rider begins to use their body differently, it is helpful to show the horse how to use its own body differently in response. Often this will happen spontaneously, but where the horse is carrying long-held physical tension or ways of moving as a result of his rider's activity, the horse needs to be shown how it, too, can change.

During joint horse and rider sessions, energy therapy can be used to maintain a state of relaxation of muscles that habitually want to tense; and to allow the mind to stay relaxed and open, rather than going over old ground. You can work on yourself in this way by directing energy to the part of your body where the problem is – ideally on the end of a lunge or when being led. As your body releases tension and pain, and parts of your body that had been held in a certain way begin to let go, you can experiment by beginning to use yourself in a new way, to work through the places where you were getting 'stuck' before. It helps to have someone watching you from the ground who can give you feedback on what you feel – people often think that their bodies are doing something far more dramatic than they actually are, because it feels unfamiliar. Sometimes it can be helpful to use calming essential oils that help to release the associated mental tension.

It is important, too, to learn some new ways of visualising or thinking about riding. It helps to find out how you, or anyone else you are treating, predominantly process information; for example, if you are someone who visualises easily. We all give clues through our language. People who think visually use terms like, 'you see what I mean?' or, 'look', before explaining something. 'Visual' people benefit from being given visual images or ideas to think of in terms of their riding. Auditory people ('I can hear what you're saying'; 'listen…',) often learn more easily when given rhythms or sounds.

Ultimately, it is also important to learn to use your senses differently and to include touch as part of your repertoire of information processing. A good starting point is to begin to introduce words about feel, or exercises that involve touching part of your own body or your horse's body as he works, and to describe feelings by making shapes with your hands.

The methods outlined here all apply to working to find new ways of handling horses, where you are treating your horse for behavioural issues. I believe it is vitally important to show people who ride and handle horses how to work with their horses in a new way from the ground. This is the key to preventing the re-occurrence of the same old problems when the horse goes home. Sometimes, if riders keep handling the horse in the same way as before, the horse is likely, in turn, to respond in the same way as he did before, and in this way old behaviour patterns can arise. This kind of relapse tends only to happen in the most basic of situations, however; and where horses are subject to the strongest provocation; for example, if a horse that was referred for biting is suddenly fed titbits again at home.

It is important to learn new ways of reacting to cues from our animals, to handle any new situations as they arise, as well as to put

Riders love to feel and see their horses become calm under the touch of a hand ...

... and reach a relaxed state within moments.

This kind of work can help riders to understand their horse's habitual posture and movement during ridden work, and to see where tension or imbalance are causing issues.

ourselves in their minds, to go some way towards preventing new problems from arising.

A key to well-being: body as a symptom of mind

Much of the time, people simply want healing for their physical condition, and wish to look no deeper than the relief of the symptoms or pain. That's fine. However, where long-term well-being is the aim, it can be beneficial to look below the surface to deal with the issues that cause imbalances and negativity in the first place, and to develop a whole-system approach. Once the healing process is underway, it can be beneficial to introduce other elements, one at a time, when necessary. I might recommend using herbs, crystals, essential oils, homoeopathy, meditation or visualisation as part of the long-term process. Rmember, though, that some of these are still just 'medicines' for 'symptoms'.

I believe that a responsible practitioner should also be in a position to offer some form of creative listening as part of the process, as and if necessary. This is not about offering advice or an opinion, but about providing an unconditional environment within which people can talk, confidentially, about their issues. Because talking is, for people, a form of release, it occurs naturally, both during and after treatment. The healing process often takes the form of talking and treatments alongside each other because physical dis-ease* is inextricably bound up within the well-being of the mind and emotions. This may be because of the way that we come to use our bodies as the result of what we believe – lots of riders who have been told they are tense become so worried about it that the whole problem becomes compounded.

There are lots of ways to understand how your body manifests what is going on in your mind. The emotional–physical relationship may, as discussed earlier, be as a result of the effect of negative energy affecting our own energy, creating disruptions and blockages. The brain is perfectly capable of affecting the body's immune system, through suppressing the production of disease-fighting white blood-cells, following a traumatic event[3]. If our immunity is low, as a result of our emotions, it's no wonder we can get sick. There is even measured proof that where the vibration of the energy field is low, there is always disease[1]. Many doctors will tell you that a lot of the illnesses their patients suffer are stress-related.

The point is, though, that if we can make ourselves sick, we can also

---

* This term is used to imply any negative physical condition.

Riders' tensions can be gently released to help find a new way of working with their horses.

make ourselves well. Visualisation has been proven as an effective cure of physical sickness, and meditation has been shown to lower blood pressure, so both of these techniques are powerful in helping the body to heal itself. You can learn both of these simple but powerful techniques for yourself, with a little patience and time. During meditation, your breathing and heart-rate slow, production of alpha-waves in the brain increase, and there can be marked changes in hormone levels as well as psychological changes. Regular meditation can even increase your energy levels and you can use it before a competition as a relaxing energy boost.

Louise Hay's book, *You Can Heal Your Life*,[4] discusses the concept that emotional fears and negativity, if not successfully dealt with, manifest themselves physically in various related parts of the body. For example, the knees are the part of our physical body which help to move us forward, so where there is reluctance to move forward mentally, due to fear or inflexibility, this can manifest itself in the knee area. I have seen one case where this theory certainly seemed to fit. I treated a young woman (in her early thirties), who had been very active, riding and competing two horses in riding-club events and show jumping.

Over the course of several years, she began to suffer all kinds of degenerative problems in her knees. She eventually had to stop riding completely, because the pain and lack of mobility in her knees made it difficult for her to sit or stand easily, let alone muck out, or cope with the repetitive motions of riding. Her doctor referred her to a specialist for an operation; but she was told she would have to wait eighteen months to two years for her surgery. In the meantime, she decided to try energy therapy. I treated not just her knees, but her whole body, and at the same time we talked about her life. It turned out that she had been in the same, fairly poorly paid job, where she wasn't particularly happy, for the past ten years. She hadn't had a relationship since her last break-up about five years previously, in spite of plenty of invitations from eligible men. She was still living with her parents, never having left home. Even her competitive work with her horses had ground to a halt, jumping at the same venues, in the same classes, over the same tracks, and riding the same dressage tests, over and over again.

As she came for treatments, the young woman made it clear that she was thinking about moving out of her parent's home, but didn't know how she would cope on her own. She wanted a new relationship, but

Relaxing and releasing tense muscles during a session can help riders to recognise and alter postural problems.

was afraid of getting involved again. She would have liked a new job but didn't know whether she would be any happier. She would like to try riding in some new classes and new dressage tests, but wasn't sure she was up to it. Basically, although she was far less than happy with her life, she was terrified of change and of actually making any moves to go forward in her life, so she had been stuck for the last five years.

We talked about what she most wanted – to ride again. We used energy therapy and visualisation – she saw herself confidently riding a dressage test she had never ridden before, thoroughly enjoying the whole thing and winning – as a way to improve her confidence and belief in a brighter future. We did some exercises on a static horse, just to give her the pleasure of sitting in a saddle. As her health improved, she began to address one element of her life at a time, and first bought her own little starter-home. This gave her the confidence and, in fact, the need to change jobs – she found a new position closer to her new home and nearer to the stables (barn) where her horses were. She even found a new boyfriend and began to feel much happier and positive about life.

Throughout this process of change, her knee problems subsided to the point where she was once again competing with her horses twice a week. Some people would say that I didn't just treat her knees, I treated her whole approach to life. Although it is important to be gentle with yourself when addressing the emotional issues behind a physical problem, it is in fact an important part of the healing process.

The language of dis-ease

The key to many of the physical conditions we manifest can be found in the language that we use. I have talked about the words we use to describe an 'unconscious' feeling registered upon interaction of our energy field with that of another person, and how we give language clues about the way we think, through speech. Now, consider the phrases we use when talking about issues in our lives that affect our bodies. We talk about 'shouldering a burden', 'shouldering responsibility', or having the 'weight of the world on our shoulders'. Perhaps, therefore, it isn't a surprise to find out that many overwhelming issues of stress are held in the shoulder area.

However, the 'life-issue' is not so much the problem, as our attitude to it, which is what is more likely to cause a physical symptom. It is as well to bear the idea of our own thought patterns, or negative emotions, in mind when working to promote harmony between ourselves and our horses. The power of positive thought can make a vast difference to the way in which we perceive our lives, either as a burden, or an opportunity.

I see examples of this in the riders who bring horses that are labelled as 'difficult' to me for healing energy therapy. It is not the horse that is difficult, it is the human who has the 'difficulty'. There is no such thing as 'difficult' horses, they are simply horses which we feel more, or less, able to handle and ride. One 'difficult' horse I recently treated went to a new owner who thought him an absolute sweetheart!

Mind power – holding and releasing dis-ease

The value of the mind in overcoming our own particular issues should never be underestimated. There are many well-documented cases of 'terminal' patients who have made astounding recoveries almost through sheer willpower. Conversely, many practitioners of the healing arts come across individuals who actually don't want to get better. I'm pleased to say this rarely happens with horses; they are always happier when they feel better again. People, however, are quite a different matter and will do all kinds of things to sabotage their own recovery.

As you tackle your own issues, it's worth asking yourself if, in fact, this might be you. It may sound harsh, but it's truer than many people realise. This kind of situation occurs through fear; of not knowing what one will become, or how one will behave, if one becomes well. The way to work through this situation is to face the fear first.

We have considered the concept that illness, pain and dis-ease can be considered an outward manifestation of an issue going on in the mind. Sometimes, the issue isn't that complicated, and may even be operating on a conscious level, for example when people have learned that they can get attention though illness.

I will never forget, after an endurance competition once, lining up with other riders to receive our rosettes before we went home. We were all packed up, our horses were loaded, and we were exhausted but happy with our achievements that day. As we stood in line, the girl next to me said, 'I'm aching all over, my back's killing me. I'm going to feel terrible tomorrow.' She had a real air of suffering about her, 'poor me'. I was shocked, partly because we had all ridden hard that day and all of us were shattered; it was one of those things that we just took as read and didn't bother mentioning. And partly, because she had the air of complaint, as though somebody else was to blame for her aches – when she had competed for pleasure, through her own choice!

The more she moaned, the more people began to make sympathetic noises. This is a simple example of learned, manipulative behaviour.

Sure, the rider in question was aching, but we all were. It hadn't even occurred to the rest of us to talk about our own aching muscles, because we just didn't need to. What did she have to gain by talking about it? Attention!

Many people use their aches, pains and illness in the same way, to gain the attention that they feel they need, or deserve. This kind of pattern develops through childhood; if a child is given lots of sympathy and special treatment when they are ill (or feign illness), the behaviour continues through adulthood. I often point out to people that, if they learn simply to ask for the attention they need, they get it and they don't have to feel ill (or exhibit any other kind of manipulative behaviour) – what could be better? This simple fact has often just not occurred to people who have learned differently. A simple fact, maybe, but it can certainly have some profound effects upon the body and the behaviour.

For long-term well-being, it is important to face such issues within our own bodies and the feelings behind them, to release them and to move forwards. Sometimes, behavioural patterns and psychological 'need' for sickness have become so ingrained, it can be scary to let go. I have worked with many riders who, just as they seemed on the verge of being completely fit and healthy, would suddenly relapse, or complain of a different set of symptoms. This can really keep a body stuck. It's worth realising that if, in fact, you take your burdens out and look at them, they are released and you can go forward lighter, happier, more freely and without having constantly to carry our emotional baggage around.

Healing energy therapy can help us to identify and release both our physical conditions and the emotional issues behind them – as well as giving us the energy to move forward. Some riders who present with back problems that affect their horses, end up changing their whole lives to eliminate what was, in fact, a muscular symptom of tension-reaction, and not a physical back condition at all. Energy therapy also helps to give new vitality and inner strength, giving people the energy to learn new physical and mental pathways of behaviour and response to thoughts, feelings and everyday situations.

By addressing the whole-person, we are following (in our own way) the ancient traditions of balancing the person as well as treating the dis-ease. In other words, we treat not just the knee, but the lifestyle so that, with the life in balance, the knee will regain and maintain full health. We treat not just the rider's aching shoulder muscles, but the attitudes, so that with the mind in balance, the whole system improves in health.

Healing yourself

The aim for lifelong well-being encourages many riders to learn to work with energy for their own benefit. This can be an illuminating process. Working with energy can help us to become more aware of, and sensitive to, the issues surrounding illness in our own bodies. The process is all about becoming aware of, or 'bringing into consciousness' aspects of ourselves which we can work to improve; whether through our riding, our ways of handling our horses, or our ways of maintaining our own health and that of our animals. Such aspects might be every-thing from body awareness and the factors behind our health and well-being, to mental/emotional awareness and the way in which we feel about the events in our lives. In being aware of our bodies and their intrinsic connection with our minds, we gain the insight and therefore the opportunity to influence the way that we act and react, positively changing for the better.

Whether you just want to improve your riding, to be able to treat your horse's aches and pains, deepen the relationship between yourself and your animals, or address your own health and well-being, energy therapy can provide significant benefits.

All kinds of issues can prevent riders from working effectively with their horses, and the horses respond accordingly. Perhaps, in the future, a new way forward will be found where the balance of the individual, whether person or animal, will be addressed in the most complete of holistic terms, the boundaries of which we are only just beginning to perceive. Perhaps we can start by forgetting the distinction between physical and emotional healing.

Case Studies

Riders and horses of all kinds can benefit from energy therapy. In this chapter, I will give some examples of different cases where energy therapy has been used to help in a variety of situations. I hope this will help people who want to work to treat their horses or their own conditions. The cases I have worked with are too numerous to cite here; besides which, the rule of client confidentiality limits those I can discuss in any depth. Here, we have everything from a very 'ordinary' horse and rider, a pony with a physical problem, a horse with a mixture of physical and behavioural issues, a 'shoot or sell' case, and a competition horse, among others. The problem doesn't have to be a major one to benefit from this kind of work, though, and I have included one or two shorter, condensed case histories, too.

Boris – physical pain and behavioural problems

Boris was an 18hh, eight-year-old Hanoverian gelding who had been used as a hunter. His new owners had found him in a field, abandoned by his previous owner. Boris was very thin and very unhappy, but was lucky that Ann and Geoff had decided to take him on and give him a chance. However, they had got to the point where they were quite scared of him, and understandably so. When I first met him, Boris attacked anyone who came near his stable. He would throw himself at the door and bite, kick anyone who got inside, corner people who carried buckets, and was extremely difficult to rug up or tack up. He was also severely underweight and arthritic; he drank very little and was almost constantly dehydrated.

Boris was exhibiting a variety of behavioural patterns that he had learned in order to manipulate the behaviour of his handlers. He was aggressive until fed and then, once he had his feed, he was aggressive until he was left alone. He didn't want to be handled and in fact, was very withdrawn from people. His behaviour had been learned in the same way that most horses learn – through reinforcement. Boris was thin and probably hungry, and as a result had become very 'competitive' around food. Behaving aggressively encouraged his owners to feed him and run rather than risk being bitten; he made sure he got the food he wanted and that there was no competition for it. Some of the staff would even throw their buckets at him to keep him away.

His kicking and aggression was a defence mechanism against being handled at all – due to the combination of a damaged back (his spine was curved and he had old saddle sores) and the pain of his arthritic hocks, which became very uncomfortable during and after hard ridden work. If Boris was aggressive, people left him alone and he was free from pain.

It wasn't enough for his new owners simply to be kind to him because, by then, his behaviour had become compounded. Even the sight of a person would send him flying at the door in an attempt to get the food he craved, and keep the pain away. Hardly an ideal situation for any owner to be in, particularly when Ann and Geoff had taken Boris on because he had been abandoned. His owners were stumped over what to do next.

First, I worked on just walking up to Boris's stable (stall) and gaining safe, unthreatening contact with him. I used to treat him with energy from a distance until contact could safely be made with his shoulder and head. Then, I gave him treatments to calm and relax him, and let him know, by physical demonstration, that I meant no harm, but that I was not prepared to be bullied. His feeding times and the vessels he was fed in were varied, in order to break his habitual 'snapping for feed' – he was treated as he ate, so that he relaxed and learned that biting was unnecessary. I also increased his feed, giving him a whole bale of hay every day, and regular small hard feeds, so that his need to 'compete' for food was eliminated.

After a few days, Boris began to calm down, relax and was reassured that people were, in fact, fairly pleasant to have around. Gradually, he allowed myself and others to enter the box (stall) and give energy therapy treatments over his entire body, including his back and hocks. This in itself took time, because at first he would try and kick when handled. He reacted very strongly to the treatments, often lying down, and began to show a marked physical and behavioural improvement within a week: he gained weight, was no longer dehydrated, was happy to be approached, touched, and rugged-up; and the clicking sounds and apparent discomfort from his hocks began to subside. Boris had, at last, learned to relax.

Boris received three treatments every week for a month, then two

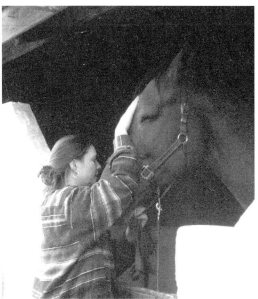

Boris. Beginning treatment – first touch and the horse begins to close his eyes but is still alert.

As he relaxes, his eyes close and his head begins to drop.

treatments weekly longer-term. I used lavender oil around his stable (stall) to relax and calm him (he chose it from a number of calming oils offered), and a specially blended Bach Flower remedy to help him release his old emotional negativity; as well as herbs to help with his arthritis. He had several months' rest without being ridden, to allow his mind and body to recover, before he was fitted with a new saddle and asked to begin gentle ridden work again. Throughout his 'rest' time, I worked with him on the ground, handling him, loose-schooling him, leading him, gently lungeing him, and turning him out as much as possible to rebuild his muscles and improve his attitude to life. I also used physical therapy and massage techniques to encourage him to use his arthritic legs in a way that he would find less painful.

The long-term, ingrained habits that Boris has acquired are not easy to clear, particularly because he had been hit and shouted at as part of his daily routine. Always a dominant horse, Boris will never be easy to handle, partly due to his size and agility, and partly due to his character. His owners will always have to work with him carefully. However, he is a healthy, relaxed and generally happy character today. His aggressive tendencies have abated to the point where he no longer kicks or bites, although he still makes the odd awful face. As a result of his therapy, he happily plays with buckets, completely ignores the process of being rugged up and is usually more than pleased to enjoy any kind of attention – including being ridden.

It was important, too, that I worked with Boris's owners and conveyed my handling methods to them when rehabilitating the horse back into their care. They had sent him to us because they had become afraid and, with a horse that is naturally dominant, being afraid just isn't helpful. Ann and Geoff's old habits of backing off whenever he threatened them, and trying to pacify him with praise, were just as hard to break as the habits Boris had learned. It was understandable, though, that they had always decided to 'stop for the time being' whenever Boris challenged them. They just needed to gain confidence and learn how to work with him.

Throughout Boris's rest and treatment, Ann and Geoff regularly came to visit Boris and to groom, lunge or loose-school him. I worked with Ann and Geoff to show them that actually, Boris was perfectly safe, but that they had to maintain the status of 'lead horse' in order to prevent him from challenging their authority. This meant using body language and appealing to his natural equine instincts whenever he threatened them – playing the predator or lead horse works perfectly in cases like this. They also had to learn to reserve praise for when it was due – instead of reinforcing his habits by praising him when it wasn't.

Boris is a handsome horse who works beautifully under saddle. He is, however, intelligent and dominant; if handled carefully, he is an excellent riding horse, but he will never be a family pet! However, Ann works with energy therapy herself, so continues to treat both Boris and herself regularly.

Millie's story – fear

Alison rang me because she had concerns about one of her daughter's horses, a nine-year-old, 15.3hh Thoroughbred mare called Millie. Millie was a show jumper, who had competed to a high standard under the guidance of professional jockeys on the stud where she was bred. Alison bought Millie for Kate, her daughter, as a schoolmistress, to take her on to higher levels of competition than Kate's current horse was capable of. Kate was a good rider and had tuition from her instructor twice a week. For a while, she and Millie competed quite successfully. However, Millie began to stop unpredictably at jumps which were by no means overfacing her and, eventually, refused to go anywhere near a pole, even on the ground. Alison and Kate had tried everything they could think of to encourage the mare to jump again. Finally, Millie had stopped so many times, tipping Kate off, that Kate had simply had enough – she

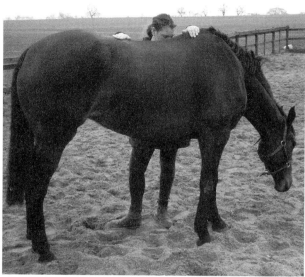

Millie *(above and opposite)* – at first it was a case of simply asking her to remain quiet in the arena, then very gradually re-introducing her to poles on the ground.

didn't want to ride the horse any more.

Having ascertained that there was nothing physically wrong with Millie, I watched as Alison led her in hand around the school at home. The mare was particularly frightened of hitting her feet on poles and once she had, would panic and back away, refusing to go anywhere near a pole again. I decided to treat her with energy therapy and see how she reacted when faced with poles in a relaxed, unpressurised situation. I gradually treated Millie so that she was relaxed and used to receiving healing treatments in the stable (stall), before moving to the sand school to treat her outside. Once she was calm enough to work on in the open, I carefully introduced poles on the ground, all the while using energy therapy to keep her relaxed and happy. After a week, Millie was happily walking through patterns of poles in a relaxed and happy frame of mind, in spite of knocking her feet, and without any treatment at all. This was quite a major leap forward for a horse that had such an adversity to poles a week previously, and wouldn't even come to within ten feet of one.

Next, I concentrated on loose-schooling Millie over poles on the ground, initially using energy therapy to relax her, and then just in her natural state. Once she was happily trotting and cantering over ground-poles loose in the school, I introduced wings next to the poles lying on the ground, then began to build little courses of fences, not more than

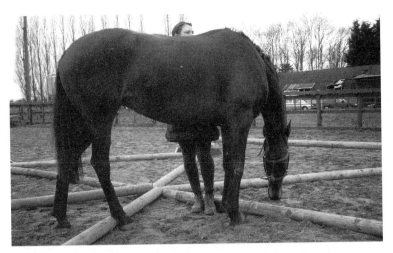

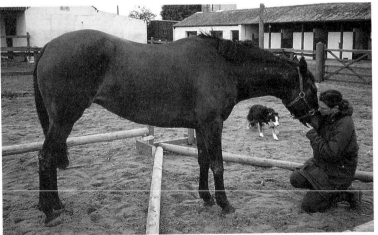

Millie back at home during her first session, with a happy rider.

six inches high, for her to work round. This stage took some time to work through, and I placed poles diagonally, on the ground, or at a strange angle next to a fence. All the while, I treated her with energy during our sessions with poles – my aim was to maintain Millie's relaxed state so that she could learn to enjoy jumping again, and realise that it wasn't a threat. I even worked her alongside a little pony who loved jumping – as a schoolmistress for Millie to 'play chase' over the fences with. Then, gradually, I introduced tack and a rider, and asked Millie to walk around a tiny course of fences, continuing to use energy treatments to maintain her relaxation and calm.

At the end of three weeks, I could bring Millie out of the stable (stall), tack her up, climb on, and walk, trot and canter her around a small course of fences, without her panicking or stopping, and with her ears pricked forward the whole way. I also worked with Kate, to show her a new way to ride Millie. The pair's old instructor seemed to have compounded, if not triggered, the problem of stopping by recommending that a naturally 'long and low' horse be ridden in a very rounded outline. Millie had been ridden into fences on a short rein and with a very strong contact – almost pulling her up before she took off. Millie had a very good mouth and was a really responsive ride, so we worked to find a way of giving her the stretch and freedom to carry herself naturally, in a relaxed style.

This way of working increased Millie's confidence, showing her that she could trust her rider to allow her to go forward, and let her use herself over a fence. It also served to increase Kate's confidence to ride Millie over fences, and led her to completely rethink her riding. Kate learned to adapt different styles to the different horses she rode, so that they would each be ridden as it best suited them, gently tapping their natural abilities and bringing them to the fore, and listening to the signals each horse gave her about how best to ride it. Luckily, Alison and Kate were bright and caring enough to want what was best for their horses, so that they could work happily with them.

Throughout the time I worked with Millie, however, it was evident that she was not a horse who loved jumping. The contrast was clear between her attitude and that of the little schoolmistress we used; our pony would fly round the fences, without any human intervention, as soon as she was let into the school, thoroughly enjoying the whole game. Millie, however, would stand quietly at one end, avoiding the fences, and would clearly rather not jump unless asked, even though she was no longer afraid. She was a sweet-tempered, gentle, but sometimes exuberant mare, who much preferred going out, hacking around the countryside and particularly, as many Thoroughbreds do, travelling very fast in straight lines. She was a very intelligent mare who had clearly been jumped to the point of total boredom in the past, and needed variety in her life. As a young, fit horse, she also needed a regular work programme, to utilise her energy and prevent her from becoming overly fresh when ridden.

Millie went back to Alison and Kate, who thoroughly enjoyed riding her over fences again at home for the next couple of weeks. However, they agreed that Millie just didn't really enjoy jumping; she would do it now if they asked her, but only because she had to. They decided that, as they would rather not force the horse to do something she was unhappy with, they would show her under saddle, and ride her in dressage competitions instead. They still pop her over the occasional fence, but only to make sure that Millie's old fears remain in the past and don't resurface – a way of maintaining her new-found confidence.

The outcome was a happy one. Post-treatment, Millie had relaxed and opened up enough to be a real companion to Kate. They bonded, and Kate wanted to keep her in spite of the fact that she had to change her aims for the horse, and work with her in a completely different discipline than the one she had intended.

Alison, who has a great interest in natural therapies, has since learned to use energy therapy for herself. She always felt that she should be doing 'something' with her hands, and found that energy therapy was the answer – what had been missing. She now regularly treats her horses, Kate (formerly a total sceptic), her dogs and the rest of the family – and reports some quite startling results.

The 'shoot or sell' youngster – tension

Valley's owner, Pippa, rang me in tears, as a last resort; the vets had said her horse had a mental problem and should be shot. Valley was a six-year-old, 15.1hh lightweight riding horse who had been bought to show under saddle. He was displaying all kinds of behaviour that Pippa was struggling to cope with; he refused to be caught, was difficult to tack up, unpredictable to ride, wouldn't load, and was a very fussy eater. Pippa had been through the whole gamut of physical diagnostics, but vets could find nothing wrong with Valley, suggesting that he was simply 'unhinged'. Everyone had pronounced the horse 'crazy', because his back, teeth, feet, physical health, environment and diet were all fine. His owner felt she had a very difficult horse on her hands and that she was failing, in spite of having consulted a series of experts.

When I first visited this unhappy pair, my aim was simply to observe. First, Pippa had to catch her horse – a long, drawn-out process even in a tiny paddock. He stood at the back of the stable (stall) and, when she went in to start tacking him up, he ran round and round, finally threatening to kick. He jumped and jostled as she tacked him up, then fidgeted uncontrollably while she mounted. Under saddle, he worked quietly for a few minutes before suddenly clamping his tongue over the bit and rushing flat-out around the arena, ignoring all aids to slow down or stop, until finally his owner wrestled him to a mutually sweaty halt. When faced with a trailer, he wasn't going anywhere near it, in spite of having been regularly loaded and travelled to shows in the past.

Clearly, this was a horse with a lot of issues, none of which had improved anything more than short-term after re-schooling by many expert trainers, and all kinds of therapy. Pippa, an experienced rider who had a shown a string of successful horses at national level, was outwardly doing nothing 'wrong'. She had worked with trainers to improve her riding and handling in an effort to find new ways to solve her problems with Valley. One thing she had come to believe was that anyone who had tried to force or 'discipline' her horse into doing anything had not achieved any lasting effect. She had also felt increasingly uncomfortable about the series of gadgets that she had been advised to employ, each peculiar to a new trainer, to 'make the horse behave' at home. These included everything from training headgear for the horse, to ropes, sticks, halters, bridles, bits – even gadgets which made a noise, that she was supposed to use whenever the horse did something he shouldn't.

As it turns out, it was a good job she felt that way; because we finally got to the root of Pippa and Valley's problems. One of their main issues was the downward spiral they were stuck in – stress causing problems, causing more stress and so on. Pippa's body carried a lot of tension and, though she didn't think they were important, she had a lot of aches and pains. I felt that horse and owner were best separated for a while. We worked this way until both had released enough tension to come together without expecting a repeat performance of all the old issues and preparing themselves for battle again. I treated horse and rider with energy therapy to relax and calm them, gradually releasing old tensions, and re-introducing each formerly problematical situation with a different rider for the horse, and a different horse for the rider.

As we gave Valley a new lease of life, he unwound, began to come out of himself and turned out to be a really nice character. Under production for showing, he had been constantly rugged with more than one layer, and was rarely turned out for longer than an hour or two (never with another horse). He was booted and bandaged, trimmed, clipped and bathed to an almost un-natural polish and hadn't ever been allowed just to be a horse. Pippa, on the other hand, had got so hung up on producing Valley in spite of being tight for time, that she began to lose her temper whenever he fiddled as she worked with him – partly because of her own physical fatigue. She was in the habit of snipping something off Valley almost every day, which he clearly hated, before jumping on his back and expecting him to work through a series of progressively more intricate schooling exercises. The pains Pippa had in her own body meant that her riding was often tense or slightly unbalanced, which Valley appeared well aware of.

Our 'root' problem was a very sensitive owner, unhappy because of pressures at work and home, with her horses as her only recreation. The equally sensitive horse saw his owner just once a day, when she was uptight, pushed for time, and expected him to provide her with a short and intense period of pleasure as she worked him in his allotted time-slot between two other horses. This was a tall order for a horse that needed more attention and less constant pressure to achieve, but needed to feel part of a herd. It was also a tall order for a woman who, struggling with the pressures of life, wanted to prove that she could achieve to the same high level with her new horse as she had with her two older horses.

Pippa and Valley both enjoyed their therapy so much that they couldn't wait to get on with life together again. At the end of their therapy, Pippa's energy levels had improved and her body felt fit and well again; she had learned to relax and enjoy her beautiful horse without having constantly to force the issue of achieving something every day. Valley, the gentleness and intelligence of his true character finally being allowed to unfold, looked forward to the attention and companionship of his owner. They have begun showing again, but without the military regime of schooling and production at home. The pair now delights in nothing more demanding than spending an evening messing about together, or exploring their local area at weekends. The horse is pleased to be caught, co-operates beautifully under saddle, eats properly and walks up the ramp of his trailer alone.

This was a case of an uptight, 'difficult' horse that was about to be sold on by an uptight rider. However, due to Pippa's bravery and willingness to face the issues between them, they've climbed back up the spiral towards happiness and well-being. All of this has been achieved without force, fear, or pain, and with the added bonus of having let go of old patterns of behaviour.

The 'ordinary' horse and rider – back problems

Bella is a 15.2hh, twelve-year-old bay cob mare, used mainly for hacking in the winter and occasional shows and fun activities in summer. Her owner, Verity, has had Bella since she was five and has been through the usual issues that horse owners face – occasional lameness, slight saddle-fitting problems, the odd fright, but nothing major. However, Verity suffered from lower back pain and found that, during painful periods, her riding suffered and Bella became distinctly one-sided. The pain in her back caused Verity to tense the muscles on one side of her body almost to the point of solidity; as a result, she shortened that side of her body, putting all her weight through the opposite hip. The problem began to manifest itself as she continually lost one stirrup, or made Bella sweat more on one side than the other. Eventually, Bella had begun to respond by carrying herself the same way, and Verity now found that Bella's way of going sometimes even brought on her own back pain. Verity had been to a physiotherapist, a chiropractor and an osteopath, but had found no lasting relief.

Verity decided to learn how to use energy therapy, having attended a lecture/demonstration and offered Bella as a guinea-pig. She was surprised at how Bella reacted to, and obviously enjoyed, her treatment, and Verity decided that she would like to experience treatments with energy therapy for herself, as well as giving Bella treatments at home. I worked to treat both Verity and Bella, to release the pain in their muscles and teach them how to work together in a more balanced way. Bella's back responded to treatment very quickly, almost visibly re-balancing itself over the course of several treatments. We worked with an exercise routine designed to encourage her muscles to develop as evenly as possible in future. Verity was also keen to work through the issues behind her back pain, to prevent future recurrence of the condition.

Since taking her first level of training with energy therapy, Verity has begun treating Bella as part of the daily routine and reports that the mare's moods and temperament, though never a problem, are far more even and calm. She also feels that using energy therapy allows her to pick up on any potential problems and treat them before they surface. Verity regularly works on her own back and finds that treating herself provides instant relief from pain, enabling her to vastly improve her riding. As a result, Bella's bouts of one-sidedness have disappeared completely and Verity's back pain is gradually subsiding.

Recovering from injury

Sky is a 14hh, sixteen-year-old grey pony gelding, used for dressage, cross-country and Pony Club activities. His thirteen-year-old rider, Becky, came home from school one evening to find Sky standing on three legs near the fence in his field, his back legs covered completely in mud and with a swollen cut to his chest. The vet was called and he treated Sky's chest-wound, telling Becky and her mother that his was a typical 'slide-and-stop' injury – Sky seemed to have run into the fence during a bout of playing in the field and simply been unable to stop in time. He was holding one hind leg awkwardly and had clearly landed on that side quite heavily. Becky was advised to rest Sky for a week until the pain subsided and his wound had begun to heal.

However, after a week's box-rest, Sky's hind leg showed no improvement although his chest-wound was recovering well. The vet decided to X-ray. There was no bone damage, but Sky had clearly damaged his leg more severely than originally thought. The ligaments and muscles surrounding the hip and sacroiliac on one side had clearly been damaged on impact, resulting in a moderate degree of constant pain. Sky rarely put weight on the affected leg and began to show signs of compensatory muscle strain and lameness elsewhere in his body as a result. Becky was given anti-inflammatory drugs and a pain-killing injection for Sky, and asked to keep him in his stable (stall) for a further six weeks. The veterinary prognosis was for a slow recovery, involving extra care and, ideally, exercises to help rebuild the damaged muscles. It was thought that Sky would suffer a degree of loss of movement in the leg, as he was advancing in years and his injury could not be treated with anything other than rest.

Becky's family was clearly concerned about Sky. He was unsettled in his box (stall), pottering around on three legs, and getting up and down many times each day as his three other legs seemed to tire. I scanned Sky's body to feel the places where he pulled more energy than others, and then worked to treat him with energy therapy around the damaged hind leg. Not only did he become far more relaxed and stop pacing around his stable (stall) but, after four weeks, had become sound. His treatments were cut down to one a week. He was walked in-hand and turned out in a small paddock next to his friends for short periods every day for the fourth week, by which time he was strong enough to go out in the main field again. He stayed sound, and enjoys a treatment every few weeks to help him stay in peak condition.

Other horses and riders I have treated with energy therapy simply for short-term work include those outlined below:

Stale, not sick

Teddy is a Shire/Thoroughbred gelding who had gone off both dressage and jumping. His owners were convinced there was something physically wrong with him; he was simply bored and tired of the same old routine. I treated him with energy therapy to increase his energy levels and lift his apparently depressed state. Teddy started going to dressage-to-music competitions instead, which he thoroughly enjoyed.

Injured and irritated

Toby is a beautiful Connemara/Arab/Thoroughbred-cross gelding. He was terrified of almost everything except standing still in his box (stall), as the result of an awful background. His current owner, extremely kind and considerate, tended to handle Toby with kid gloves and avoid any situation that scared him. His main fears were of ropes and straps of any kind, as he had been involved in an accident where he had bolted down a main road with a lunge-line attached to his headcollar (halter). During this fearful episode, the line had become hopelessly tangled around Toby's legs and he had been hit by a car. He had clearly suffered from pain and fear as a result.

Toby associated ropes or straps with injury. Due to this fear, he was hard to catch and rug, and would not let his owner's husband put a headcollar (halter) on him. I worked with Toby to relax and calm him, introducing work with the headcollar (halter) and lead ropes as he was being treated. By the end of the second session, Toby was perfectly happy to allow his headcollar (halter) to be put on and taken off by his kind, patient owner's husband. Much to his owner's surprise, I also had ropes draped over the top of his head, round his legs, and in various parts of his body that he just wouldn't have coped with previously. Both Toby's owner and her husband have since learned to work with energy therapy for themselves, to relax and calm Toby as they work with him through his fears, and to relax and calm themselves so that they can provide the ideal environment for his recovery.

Fear of pain

Kim is a young Arab mare who wouldn't be caught for weeks on end. She had muscular damage to her back as a result of an injury that she had sustained as a foal. I worked with healing energy treatments to heal her back and calm her tension and panicking fits. I regularly caught her, gave her a relaxing energy treatment before letting her go, later slowly re-introducing ridden work. Within a short period of time, she was coming to the gate for her treatment of her own accord; her owner learned to use energy therapy for herself so that she could continue to give Kim the treat(ments) she enjoyed.

Learning to Use Energy

Who can learn?

It is a fact that **absolutely anyone** can learn to work with energy therapy. There are no pre-qualifications or prerequisites. Lots of people say to me 'Oh, but you have the healing touch; or 'I'm not like that.' Often they're afraid that they will be the one who, for some reason, can't do it. It's true that working with energy may come more naturally to some than others; but of all the people I have taught, each and every one can now draw in and project energy.

Other Eastern techniques such as Tai Chi and Qi Gong work to increase the capability of the individual to draw in and project energy. In Eastern countries, practitioners of martial arts often work as healers, too, because of their ability to sense and direct energy. These practices involve long years of exercise and training, involving rigorous practice, attention to lifestyle and exercise routines. Energy therapies, however, can be taught quickly and easily, and without risk to the student. The basic ability to draw in and project the energy is given through an 'attunement', which serves to remind your body how to tune in to, and work with, ambient energy.

Anyone can be attuned – I have even attuned horses. It is true that some people either have higher natural levels of energy or are more open to the ability to draw it in and project it, but even those who have never had leanings that way can learn. It is thought, however, that those who have the greatest empathy with others have undergone some kind of ordeal of their own which enables them to identify with others' problems. This has a ring of the ancient tribal tradition of the shaman as 'wounded healer'. However, it is certainly true that people who have undergone some kind of illness or trauma of their own find that it brings about the realisation that life is for living, and that it's much too short for being sick. This kind of experience can be used to help other people find the way to health.

What are the benefits?

As with any new skill, you can enjoy the benefits of working with energy to whatever degree you wish. For those who want to self-treat, the benefits include an increase in energy levels and relaxation, a sense of inner strength, clarity of mind, increased awareness, and the ability to be able to recharge one's own batteries and relieve one's own pain whenever necessary. These benefits can clearly be of great advantage in terms of riding, as well as everyday life. Long-term, significant changes can take place in one's own health and quality of life.

For those who want to treat their horses, the benefits are countless. Many incorporate treatments as part of the daily or weekly routine, to improve their horse's health, energy levels and well-being. Working with energy also raises your awareness of and sensitivity to your horse's body, enabling you to pick up and treat any issues as they arise. It is wonderful to be able to positively work with energy to calm and relax a horse with a less than quiet temperament; most riders thoroughly enjoy the process of treatment and their horse's response to it.

For competition riders whose horses can be prone to tension, being able to keep your horse calm and relaxed, particularly where veterinary examinations are involved, the benefits are obvious – especially when it comes to reducing your horse's pulse-rate. The increase in the level of your awareness is of great benefit in using your own body when riding, particularly for finding new ways to deepen the connection with your horse. The ability to make contact with the horse's mind and body on a deep level is something that many riders seek, but have been unable to find a way to do.

What are the options?

There are many kinds of courses and workshops in energy therapy available all over the UK and USA and indeed, the world. I originally learned to work with Reiki, and there are variations of Reiki called Tera-Mai, Karuna, Rainbow Reiki and Seichem (although purists would say these are new forms of therapy based on Reiki, and not actually Reiki – as is my own work). There are many other forms of energy work being taught, such as Therapeutic Touch – and there are new therapies evolving, it seems, almost daily. Even spiritual and faith healers will work to help teach new people who are interested in working with healing energy. Ultimately, it is up to each of us to choose the path that most suits our own way of thinking and working. There are many teachers who offer a combination of some or all of the above.

Finding a practitioner or teacher

At present, there aren't many of us who work just with animals or horses and riders, but the numbers are growing as people expand their knowledge. I am keen to encourage people to work with animals as well as people, and run 'conversion' workshops for therapists who have never worked with animals before. There is no reason why someone who works purely on people should not treat you, your horse or any other animal just as effectively as a specialist equine therapist – their treatments should be just as beneficial. I know plenty of practitioners of energy therapy who will agree to work on horses; those who find they are frightened of close contact with horses, or are unused to working with animals, can offer to work at a distance. There can be advantages to working with a specialist equine practitioner, with a background in working with horses, so long as they maintain a non-judgemental approach.

You only have to pick up any 'alternative health' or complementary interest magazine to find lists of courses, practitioners and workshops. With the current growth of interest in this area, there is bound to be someone not far from you who can offer the kind of training you are looking for. The Internet is always a vast source of information and, even if you can't find anyone in your area who has a web site, contacting the people you do find will often lead you to someone closer to home.

Alternatively, ask around at natural healing centres, centres of alternative medicine, health food shops or at shops selling crystals, books and items of 'new age' interest; often they keep a list of workshops or practitioners in your local area. Some vets will even recommend a practitioner to you if they know of one. The best recommendation, as ever, is by word of mouth. The objective personal experiences of another rider in the same kind of situation as your own are always far more informative than the glossiest advertisement.

Once you have found a practitioner to suit you, that person might be your best option for training, so long as they are able and prepared to teach you what they know. This way, you know you already 'click' with the person, which is essential if you are going to make the most of their teaching style to absorb as much of their knowledge as you can. Personality is one of the main issues of contention between teacher and pupil, so it is worthwhile finding someone that you really get on with, whose teaching style suits your way of learning, and who will give you the time and attention that you need.

Some practitioners may be unable to teach their work, for example if they haven't yet learned to, or found a way of, teaching others; and some may be unwilling. The unwillingness to teach others is, I believe, a waste of the ability that the practitioner has.

Generally, the feeling of 'protectiveness' around one's individual knowledge arises because somebody is concerned with protecting their income, and doesn't welcome the addition of more competition in what they perceive as a marketplace. I personally am wholly against this view. I believe that it is our duty to share what we know with others, if only to help the progress of other people who want to learn, and so help the animals that people share their lives with. I take the view that I can't be in more than one place at a time, I can only treat so many horses and riders and, until everyone is able to work to heal themselves, there will never be a shortage of people to treat and teach. If the day comes that we can all heal ourselves and our horses, so much the better.

I would also issue a 'Beware of' warning about the element of complementary therapists that I term 'the flowing robes'; who are very aloof and secretive about their work, who charge high prices, and refuse to teach other than a 'chosen few'. This kind of nonsense surrounding something that we can all do is, luckily, fading fast and should not be permitted in a society where we are all working to improve our own and our horses' lives.

Some people have an issue about age when it comes to people who work with the healing arts, or with horses. People can be trained at any age and even a seventy-year-old can be a novice therapist. A young therapist may have been working with healing or horses for their entire life, whereas someone in middle age may only have come to this kind of work recently. There is a lot more to be said for having worked with animals for the whole of a young life than for the last couple of years of an older one, although maturity clearly brings benefits of its own. Many youngsters have also been taught by, or worked alongside, the older generation; I learned a fair proportion of the practice I now use daily at the hands of people who were in their seventies when I met them. I have also taught ten and twelve year olds to work with energy. As they say, don't judge a book by its cover!

In terms of training, it is up to you whether you prefer to be taught in a group workshop, singly, in pairs or as part of a small group. I started out teaching larger groups and occasionally still do for some kinds of workshops. Some students prefer the anonymity of working within a larger, less personally focused group. However, many people prefer to be taught one-to-one or with a close friend or partner. Learning to work with energy can be a very individual experience, and a teacher should have respect for the wishes of a student to work alone at first. Lots of riders also like to learn by working on their own horses at home. You are likely to find that teachers who are prepared to give you the time to work alone will also be prepared to offer backup, telephone advice and ongoing support. I feel that offering backup is being responsible, because of the changes that learning to work with energy can bring into people's lives. It is worth 'shopping around' to find the person you really click with.

The cost of learning

The prices charged by practitioners and teachers alike will vary. Some are in the enviable position of being financially secure enough to be able to work without charging; sadly these are the minority. Some such teachers truly have 'guru' status (and deservedly so) and will charge a correspondingly high fee for training. However, price is not a reflection of skill as a teacher or practitioner; simply of what people will pay.

Because energy therapy can be taught so quickly and easily, many teachers have a 'bums on seats, money in the bank' approach. I know one teacher who ran a lot of courses to large groups as soon as he was able to teach, with the sole aim of paying off his mortgage arrears! I feel there's a little more to teaching someone to work with energy than that.

Ultimately, the energy you receive will be the same if you pay a vast fee, or go to the person down the road who gets on quietly with their work and teaches you for free. You're not paying for the energy, you're paying for the whole package – it's a question of how you want to learn and experience your training. There is a movement now to make healing and energy therapy training available to as many people as possible, and most people charge what they consider to be a fair rate to cover overheads and living expenses, ignoring much of a profit element, or donating profits to equine charities. Internationally, this is reflected in attempts to 'cap' and regulate training fees

If a practitioner or teacher comes to visit your premises, you might feel you're paying a lot for an hour or two's work. However, they will have had to travel to reach you, to pay for their petrol, maintain their car, and arrange their day around your visit. An hour's treatment can, in my experience, easily involve five or six hours' work, which clearly has a knock-on effect. Where training is concerned, there will also have been a certain amount of preparation of materials prior to training you.

Some teachers and practitioners will ask you to visit them; in this case, prices charged will vary according to the premises you visit and whether they are hired, or their own home. Generally, because a visit to a teacher or practitioner is in your time and transport, the charge will be lower.

Certificates, letters and methods

The qualifications of teachers or practitioners are an issue to some, and not to others. Many people are justifiably proud of a string of hard-earned letters or titles after their name; others feel it pretentious to use them. Someone who has practised intuitively all of their lives, or whose skills may have been in the family for generations, will rarely have any formal qualification at all. Someone like this may be a more valuable teacher than anyone who has a string of qualifications but little practical experience. There is also a certain amount of ego involved with some of the titles involved in this kind of work; I prefer not to use the term 'healer' or 'master' because of this, although for many, this is what they have aspired to. Ultimately, your judgement of a therapist should be purely on the merits of how you feel about them and the work they do. Again, this is where personal recommendation is so valuable.

Membership of associations generally means little, if anything, where complementary work is concerned; simply that one has paid to become a member, although there are associations that place criteria upon membership. At the same time, many qualifications can mean little, as complementary work is so unregulated. Conversely, they may have been received from someone who has been practising all their life; my best advice is to trust your instinct. Insurance, however, is important, particularly when working with horses, unless you are asked to sign a disclaimer of the practitioner or teacher's responsibility.

Teaching methods vary a great deal from one teacher to another. Because of the way that teachers pass their information on to students, the methods and content taught changes, as generations of students add or develop the methods they were taught. The original system of natural healing as taught by Mikao Usui consisted of the energy, attunement to it, and the use of several Japanese symbols as a way of directing or using the energy. The basis of his work was about compassion for one's fellow beings; it is as well to bear this in mind and remain uncluttered by all the 'extras' that have become attached to different forms of training. The original system also had only seven hand positions, part of a standard healing system used in eastern traditional medicine long before Usui's time. Today, there are far more complicated sets of hand positions taught. Some teachers employ lots of ritual, tools and detailed information; others work in a more direct, anecdotal, informal way.

How does it work?

Reiki, the energy therapy that I learned, is generally taught in three levels or stages. I continue to teach Reiki to students who wish to learn it, or teach energy therapy 'my way', in the way that so many teachers have adapted and developed what they originally learned. Because my life has been as much with animals, particularly horses, as it has people, it is natural that I have adapted what I learned to meet the needs of my work. My additional work is not, however, a distortion of the system I was originally given, but includes extra practical and theoretical work for equine students to use, or for people who just want to work with animals. The division into three stages is purely a gradual raising of your energy levels, and the energy that you can project – not a level of attainment. It doesn't mean that someone who has second-level training is 'better' than someone who has first-level, just different. Having your own energy raised so drastically all at once would just be too much to handle!

The first level of training consists of four attunements, which gradually open up the energy centres of your body to enable you to draw in and project energy. You also learn hand positions for use, and the theories behind energy therapy. To allow the energy to settle within your body, and so that you to get used to working with energy, at least a month should be left before taking second level. Some teachers do give first and second-level attunements in one weekend. Sometimes, this is a good option, but generally only for people who have worked with energy before. Many teachers ask that you leave three months before second-level attunements; some recommend longer. It is an individual choice and depends upon your own feelings; generally, instinct will tell you when the time is right and you are ready to handle more energy. First level is about self-healing, so this is when any physical conditions that you tend to suffer from are likely to be 'kicked out'.

With second-level attunements (usually two), there is a noticeable increase in the flow of energy. Whereas first level tends to concentrate on the physical health of the person receiving the attunement, second level focuses on the emotional and mental healing in the student. The increased flow of energy makes for a stronger treatment for others. At this level, the three symbols are taught which Usui developed as 'tools' to direct the energy. With the symbols, distance healing and more specific use of the energy becomes possible. Generally, a period of at least three months, more often six or nine, should be left before taking third level.

Many people are happy with the energy they work with at either first or second level. Some people take first level, only to find that it doesn't really suit them. A great many practitioners and teachers of energy therapy are second level. Some, however, prefer to take third-level attunements and learn to attune others.

Third level gives additional attunements (one or more) and an additional symbol, which is used during the attunement process as well as during treatments. The attunements again increase the level of energy that your body can hold and project. Third level is also when you are given the attunement process, so that, after a settling period of around three months, you can teach and attune others.

If I am teaching someone who wants to treat horses or to improve their riding, I pass on as much of my knowledge based on my own experience as I can at the time of working with them, as is appropriate to that student. With each level of training, I give information about working with animals, horses and other riders, and how the energy can be used to enhance one's own riding and relationship with horses – for example, hand positions, ways of treating horses and my own experiences of working. My aim is to give students some basis on which to continue and develop their own work.

Attunements

The concept of an attunement is a strange one for anyone who hasn't experienced it. The attunement is a process which is simply a way of reminding the student that she is connected to a limitless energy system; and enables the energy to flow along the channels of the student's body. Once you have had an attunement, you will have the ability to draw in and project energy for the rest of your life. It does not wear off, and you can never lose it, although it becomes smoother and easier the more you use it. Attunements are a great healing process and start a clearance physically as well as mentally and emotionally, as the energy begins to flow more freely and strongly through you.

On a more philosophical level, the attunement process has been described as a healing of our own memory, where the knowledge survives of our ability to heal, so that our bodies remember how to draw in and project energy. Attunements are performed by the teacher over the body of the student. Some Buddhist schools still go through similar rituals called empowerments, where the recipient is given a spiritual name. There are other, similar processes in cultures elsewhere in the world. The more people in the West who are attuned to and practise energy therapy, the better, as this way we don't risk losing the ability to work with energy again.

The start of a journey

As with any course, training or qualification, the process of learning from a teacher should always be seen as the beginning of a journey. Personal, practical experience counts for everything. It may be possible to spend time working alongside your teacher, or offering to help on visits or treatments. Practice is vital and is what will give you the experience and confidence to treat yourself, your horses and other animals. We will discuss this further in the next chapter.

It should be said here that learning to work with energy therapy is not a religious process and has no dogma, unlike other kinds of healing, and requires no particular set of beliefs. It tends to fit quite well with any background and belief system; but it can certainly be a spiritual path. The process of learning about energy is one that humbles and enlightens. If you choose to use your training to work with other people and animals, you will find that you almost become simply a tool for the benefit of those around you. It's not a very glamorous life, and it can be a lonely one at times, but if it's what you enjoy doing, it can be incredibly rewarding. We will discuss 'life after training' further in the next chapter.

Energy and Your Life

Once you have the ability to work with energy, it is entirely up to you how you use it as part of your daily life. The basis of using energy is to offer it compassionately and unconditionally for the benefit of those who receive it, be they human, equine, or anywhere in between.

How do I do it?

After the attunements, all that is necessary for you to draw in and project energy is to place your hands on the body of another person or animal, with the intention of healing. The energy begins to flow automatically and is drawn to where it is most needed by the body you are working on. Once you become used to the process, you can experiment with working on plants, food, or anything you choose. You can also work with your hands directly on, or a little way away from, the body you are directing energy to, to find where it feels best for you to work. In whatever way you use the energy, the best results are achieved by simply remaining calm and relaxed and allowing it to work.

'Turning off' the flow of energy is simple; it just ceases to flow after an area has received enough, or after you remove your hands from the body you are treating. The only exception is when you will sometimes feel a 'fizzing' sensation in your hands if you come close to another body that is pulling energy in. Occasionally, though, you may find the flow begin of its own accord; sometimes, you can literally walk down a street, feel a tingle, look around and think – who needs it? It is up to you whether you offer energy to people when this happens. Energy therapy can never do harm, so you never need to worry about whether to give it or not – it is always beneficial, but bear in mind that you should work on injuries from the sides. The great advantage of working with healing energy therapy is that, every time you give a treatment, you also receive a treatment yourself as the energy flows through you. This increases your own vitality and leaves a sense of well-being.

Self-healing

Much of the time, self-healing is the main use that people make of energy therapy. If you are not using energy to treat others on a regular basis, thus receiving a 'top-up' yourself, it is important to incorporate self-treatment into your life. For riders, a good time to treat is often just

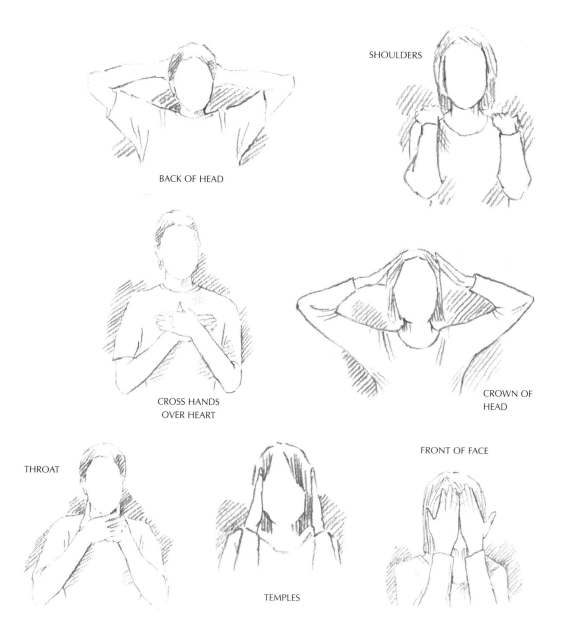

BACK OF HEAD

SHOULDERS

CROSS HANDS
OVER HEART

CROWN OF
HEAD

THROAT

TEMPLES

FRONT OF FACE

before or after riding, or when treating your horse. You can incorporate a quick five- or ten-minute session to relax and energise your own body prior to riding, as well as afterwards, at the same time as you are preparing your horse to ride. You can even treat yourself while you are riding, particularly if you feel fatigue or an ache coming on – but don't overdo it and bring yourself to the point of such complete relaxation that you aren't safe on a horse! Riders who compete can give themselves an extra boost before, during and after competing, which will help to stabilise the body, clear the mind, and raise strength and energy levels.

Many people find that the best time to treat their own body is at the beginning or end of the day, as part of their morning or evening routine. For most of us, the best time to treat is when sitting down and relaxing in the evening, or even before falling asleep at night. This is a great way to release the strains of the day and recharge your batteries for the following morning; with practice, you can literally plug the energy in and leave it to treat your body while you drift off to sleep. Needless to say, this is a great way of inducing a restful sleep, too.

Because working with energy is so inconspicuous, you can use it at any time, in any place. I have given horses a 'blast' whilst riding them, and treated myself whist sitting at a desk or in a chair, even in a room full of people. You can even treat yourself while you're standing in a

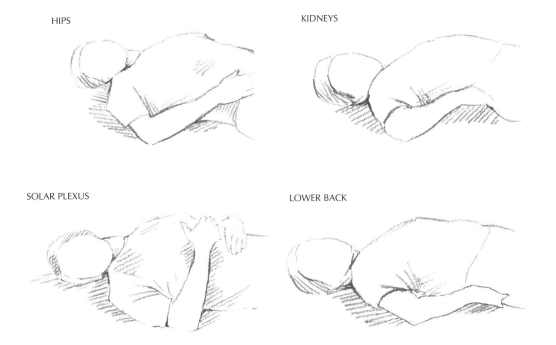

HIPS

KIDNEYS

SOLAR PLEXUS

LOWER BACK

queue or walking around a shop, simply by placing one hand on your hip. Whenever you feel under the weather, tired, sad, or anything less than good, it is reassuring to know that you can treat yourself to improve matters. The key to creating a clearer and stronger flow, as well as to making energy work positively for you in every aspect of your life, is to practise using it every time your hand touches your own body, or that of your horse or your partner; this way, it becomes automatic.

One thing that tends to happen is that, once people know about your new 'hobby', word can spread pretty quickly. Where complementary therapy of any kind is concerned, quietly getting on with what you do can have some startling results. Even if you never intended to treat anyone other than yourself and your own horse, you might find that, out of curiosity, people start asking to have a treatment, or experience the feeling of energy therapy for themselves.

Some people who learn to use energy specifically with the idea of making it a way of life, find that quite the opposite happens. You cannot 'push' for the kind of work you want to do, it just comes if it is right; at the same time, it can be a little selfish to refuse to help others if they really want you to. This is when you have to learn to be gracious enough to follow life in the direction it takes you rather than struggling against it. This may be a very Taoist view, but on the whole, it's more sensible than trying to force your way into something that ultimately, you might not be fitted for, or capable of; or of trying to hide your own talents if you have an aptitude for working with others. Life is a journey, after all, and the best way to experience it is to explore. It might not be what you thought you wanted, but new directions bring new challenges and new learning.

Ethics and intent

The idea of having ambient energy coursing through your body and being able to project it through your hands as a matter of your everyday life brings us to questions of ethics. You should always have permission from the individual you are treating; you can never force it on another living being, and attempting to do so against their will can be detrimental to your own mind and body. I have heard of those who talk about 'pushing' energy in, to 'make' a horse relax; this is absolute nonsense, as well as being wholly unethical. The body will only draw in the energy it needs, and you cannot somehow 'make' another body take energy in if it doesn't need to. People can also block energy if they really don't want to receive it, although this is rare and more a question of studiously ignoring the fact that they can feel something. If someone asks you for a treatment, or what it feels like, or asks you to treat his or her horse or animal, this is fine; permission has been given. I always mentally ask the horse I am about to work on if it is OK with them that I treat their body. Offering treatment to someone is quite different; it never seems to have the strength of effect as when they have felt motivated to ask you.

The whole basis of working with energy is the intent behind your actions; so long as your intent is for the good of the recipient of the energy, it will work to help them. It's basically about keeping yourself, or rather, your own ego, out of things; any unethical or selfish intent somehow seems to dampen the effect of treatment. Intent, and the effect it can have, is something that will become more apparent to you as you work with energy. Suffice it to say that it is the key to guiding and working with energy. One example of a misguided intent is where riders want to treat their own horses without looking objectively at what their horse is doing. In other words, it's pretty selfish if your intention is to heal your horse's leg so you can compete this weekend, when you know the leg should be given longer to recover properly. I have known people to try and heal horses with terminal illness so that they would stay alive a little longer – when the horse concerned really just wanted to let go. Another example is where riders are perhaps unaware of a bigger problem than the immediately visible one; for example, trying to treat a horse to make him behave quietly, when he might be stressed because of something you're doing.

Conversely, however, if you know that another person or animal really wants help but you don't know what's wrong, you can place your hands on the body with the sole intent of helping heal whatever the issues are. This can prove incredibly powerful and is a selfless act of intent being used to help another. Perhaps the most important point to remember is that you are not in charge; the energy does not come from you and you are not the healer. You are simply allowing the energy to come through you, for the benefit of the body receiving it. It helps to maintain a kind of calm detachment from the idea that you are projecting energy, both to aid your own balanced approach and for the benefit of those around you.

No one likes somebody who is pompous, but many people who work with energy find that, because people ask them for help, they can become rather puffed-up and egotistical with the idea that they somehow have 'healing hands', a 'gift' or some kind of 'power'. This kind of attitude leaves a bad taste in the mouth of most people, as does an overly pious attitude which makes people feel guilty for being ill or asking for help. I usually stay very quiet around the 'trumpet-blowers'.

I treated someone's horse recently who kept talking about a Reiki Master they knew of, with a capital M and an awe-struck tone, who wouldn't come and treat their horse because they were far too busy, far too expensive and anyway, they didn't work on mere animals. Needless to say, I didn't comment, remaining confident in the laws of 'karma' – what goes around, comes around!

Anyone trained to third level is entitled to use the word Master to describe what they do; I prefer not to, because people misconstrue it. In energy therapy, the term is meant as if one were a Maths master; not that you have mastered anything, rather that it has mastered you and you are simply a teacher of others. No truly genuine therapist will have any ego, show, or control issue about their work. It is simply something that is done in the same way as riding a horse, or walking the dog, or cooking the dinner; although obviously it is more profoundly moving than cooking the dinner. Many people find it hard to retain their humility when they see the effect that energy can have. However, it is vital that you do so and don't get carried away with the idea of being an 'expert', because this can seriously affect the unconditional and compassionate environment that you can offer to others. Your judgement should not enter the equation, except in the rarest of circumstances.

Helping other people

The reactions of others can be both a delight and a challenge. During the course of my work I have found that the radiant smiles following treatment, the relief of pain in horses and riders, and the progress and pleasure gained by others makes me feel truly humble and grateful to have been able to be part of the process. Sometimes, working with energy can bring humour and a fresh interest into people's lives, particularly if you are treating in public. I have one student who enjoys a treatment as she waits in the collecting ring, so I place my hands on her shoulders as she watches the competitors who ride before her. Her friends always say that I'm 'holding her up' in case she faints from pre-competition nerves!

At other times, working with people can be challenging emotionally and bring great sadness, particularly when working with terminal patients, or when a person simply decides to hold an illness and stop having treatments. Many people find it too challenging to become whole and healthy which, though we have to accept is their own choice, can be sad and frustrating. Sometimes I am worried or scared by new cases that I am presented with; I think, 'Oh no, why me?' – usually I feel like this not about people, but about another aggressive stallion or another enormous kicker! However, the 'why' is simple – you get what you get because you are the person who can help. Again, it is important to remember that it is not you who does the healing; so place your confidence in whatever higher powers you believe in, and simply allow the energy to work on the body.

The scepticism of others can be a challenge in itself. I tend not to worry about it, and believe that everyone has their own choice whether to have an interest, or belief in, the efficacy of the healing arts. I will happily explain anything to someone who asks, and can (usually) laugh along with those who choose to poke fun. Generally you will find that sceptics keep pretty quiet face-to-face but, if they want to feel the energy for themselves, I will happily place my hands on their shoulders and give them a 'blast'. Often this is the best way to convince a sceptic. People like this can become very hung-up on results and like to see an instant, miraculous cure as opposed to a gradual improvement or increased quality of life. Results are not under our control; the body responds in its own way, and anyone who promises miracles should be treated with justifiable scepticism.

Working with energy is simply about offering the energy to another; the body does with it what it will and, if the intent of the person or animal receiving treatment is to release their illness, then they will do so. If their intent is to receive comfort as they die, they will do so; and if a body really wants to stay ill, you can't force it to get better. Sometimes, 'healing' means just acceptance, not change.

Whether you treat other people, yourself, your family or your horse, supervision is important. Supervision is the concept of having someone that you can go to as back-up, to talk to and to seek advice from. Often, this will be the person who taught you; sometimes, you will meet or come across an individual that you really feel good with, can learn from and respect. The idea is basically the age-old one of taking care of oneself first. If you are not fit and well, mentally and physically, you are simply not in a position to give effective help to others – it's a bit like trying to throw someone else over your shoulder and carry them when your own leg is broken. I'm not suggesting that every professional energy therapist is perfect, simply that you have to maintain your own health in order to be an effective helper of others. We can all get sick – let's be realistic; it is sometimes even said that we experience such reminders in order to make us more able to relate to those we heal. Aside from this, it is immensely helpful to have someone more experienced that you can go to, to discuss matters, compare experiences with or seek advice from, and to give you some input once in a while.

The animal issue

Some therapists maintain a form of snobbery over treating horses and other animals. I have heard it said that animals are of a lower vibration than humans, and that therefore we should not concern ourselves with healing them, because healing mankind is far more important. Some people even say that animals don't have souls! You also come across many people who think they would like to work with animals because they can't stand people, and don't want to deal with them or hear them moaning. These issues are purely, I think, a lack of vision. Animals are incredibly spiritual beings and in some ways very altruistic; they teach us so much about how to behave and, if we could only apply these lessons to the way we treat other people, society would be less pressurised and in many ways, kinder.

Just think about the way that your dog is always pleased to see you – how many people give you such unconditional love? I like to treat animals with the respect they deserve and believe that the human animal is simply different, and not a master of the others, by any means. Studies have even shown that dolphins have more capacity for intelligence than humans. When you look at the downside of our society, with the horrific violence, competition for resources and money, exploitation of each other and our environment, it is easy to want to retreat from society completely and go swim with dolphins instead! I see animals as the companions, guardians and teachers of men – this has certainly been the case in my life and, in passing my experiences on to others, the horses that have taught me, have in turn helped me to teach others. Horses are also, thankfully, uncluttered by all the rubbish our modern world throws at us, and work on an instinctive level; if they want to be with you, they do, and if you hurt them, they show it. They demand so little from us, and put up with the kind of treatment that humans simply would not tolerate.

I feel, in line with many animal therapists and many ancient cultures the world over, that horses and other animals can teach people and encourage our development. Just think about your own interest in complementary health care, and in natural practices. So many riders become keen to find out more about interests like this because they care for their horses. If you spend a lot of time with animals, you learn a great deal about how people behave; for example, instinctive fears, emotional memory-scars, and the need for companionship and contact. I studied human psychology for a number of years, but what really brought it all into reality for me was watching the way that horses and other animals behaved, and seeing this behaviour mirrored in humanity.

Other animals are often attracted when treatments are in progress, and enjoy some work themselves. I treat dogs, cats, and many other creatures.

I was quite amazed at first; but, instead of the way that so many people 'humanise' their horses ('he's saying he wants his dinner'), it is actually far more enlightening to 'instinctualise' people. This could form the topic of a whole book in itself, so all I will say here is that, whenever you learn something about the way your horse behaves, it can be a real revelation if you apply that lesson to human behaviour.

To those who want to work with energy on horses because they don't like dealing with people, I would recommend a different path in life. Every horse is owned by, or lives with, a human. If you are unable to empathise with a person's concerns and worries, whether related to a horse or not, that person knows immediately. People often feel that there is some sort of 'special' quality necessary to work with animals and that, therefore, if they work with them, then they're special. Horses are actually far simpler, less complex and less demanding to work with than people.

Many horses have problems caused by their owners, or are mirroring their owner's behaviour, in which case you have to find a way to treat both person and animal. Some people use their horses as a way to find a therapist or, seeing the benefits their horses enjoy from treatments, become interested in self-treatment. On many occasions, I have started out treating a horse, and ended up seeing the whole family and their pets. I feel that one of the most important points about working with a horse is to improve the relationship between that creature and the person who handles it. It is, therefore, a narrow and closed mind that wants to work with animals only; compassion is not species-specific. We all have our lessons to learn, and if, for some therapists, it is that they can work with horses and not be afraid, then that's positive. If the lesson for other people is that they can work with people as well as animals and help them, then that's positive, too.

Teaching others

If you find that other people want to learn from you, this is a great compliment and a privilege. I have read in other healing books that 'knowledge is power', but if you don't do anything with it, it isn't. Personally I don't feel any need to have any kind of power, and I feel that the grace and strength of one's own experience lies in being able to pass it on to others. I don't see that there is any 'power' in knowledge, or the retention of it, at all. If I dropped dead tomorrow, I would hope that I had taught enough people and written enough down that more people could continue and develop some of what I started; not that it all be lost, surrounded by secrecy.

I never intended to be a teacher. It simply happened that, because language comes easily to me, people began to ask me to teach them. Many people want to teach because they think they would be good at it, and then find they're not, or that they don't enjoy it. Some people lack the confidence to teach others. The best advice I can offer is just to stand back and let it happen, for the good of the others involved. Much of the time, teaching is just about giving information to other people in a way that they can understand. Passing on what you know to others can be very rewarding.

Something I really enjoy is the moment when, after attunement or training, a new student first puts their hands on their own horse to project energy. In a split second, the smile on that person's face expresses the utter delight with a new-found contact between horse and rider, and the thrill of a new voyage of discovery around what had hitherto just been a body.

Building a practice

If you decide to, or if you find that you are drawn into, working with energy therapy on a professional basis, it is vital that you take out some form of insurance, to protect yourself and those you treat or teach. You should also gain at least a cursory familiarity with the laws surrounding complementary work. Currently, complementary therapists are not permitted to work on animals without the vet who would normally treat that animal being aware of what you are doing. The laws surrounding human treatment are far less strict, although in the USA, there are laws concerning work on the human spine.

Working alongside other practitioners of healing arts is a wonderful experience, particularly if you choose to share and compare knowledge and training, or attune each other to the kind of energy that you were trained to work with. The combined energy projected through more than one body can be so beneficial to those you work on, and it can be an uplifting sensation to share treatments with therapists from other schools of training. Because energy works alone, as well as aiding any other treatment or therapy, I am always keen to work with vets, farriers, chiropractors and other complementary therapists who care for horses' health. Although the climate is changing, sometimes members of the more orthodox professions aren't as open-minded. Sadly, some people still perceive complementary practitioners as a threat and will not always work with us. This basically comes down to the mistaken idea that one approach, orthodox or complementary, is right. I feel that we should combine our knowledge and be able to work together; I see no conflict.

When it comes to charging other people for your work, it is up to you to ask for what you feel to be a fair fee for your time and any overheads involved. My aim is to one day treat and train anyone for free – but the reality for most of us it that we do have to charge, because we're not in a position of being able to live for free. It is worth bearing in mind the idea of exchange; if anyone cares to barter, this can be a great way of getting hold of something you would otherwise have paid for. The important point about healing is that whoever receives it places a value on it and therefore takes some responsibility for their own healing – they must want to get better. Sometimes it helps if you ask what people would *like* to pay. One thing I have found is that 'horsey' people can be among the most difficult to get money from (and the best at pleading poverty!), particularly as you are working with something no one can see. Your time and skill should be respected in exactly the same way as anyone else's.

Working with energy can very quickly become a way of life. If you maintain your truth and intent, it can be immensely rewarding, and can teach you things you may never have otherwise learned, as well as bringing into reality a closer harmony between humans and animals. For all those who simply want to achieve a closer relationship and deeper understanding of horses, the tools have never been more readily available than they are today; it's simply a question of grasping the opportunity with both hands.

...and Finally

By the time you have finished reading this book, I hope that the idea of using energy as a healing therapy for yourself and your horse will seem less strange than it did at first.

My aim in writing this book was to bridge the gap between healing and practical applications for horses and riders. I hope, primarily, to encourage others to explore the healing arts, and apply what they learn to the animals and people around them. I also wanted to show that energy is something we can all use and benefit from in a very normal way. Often the 'myth and magic' surrounding healing puts people off approaching a practitioner, so I hope that I have brought it a little more into the common domain. It is important to me that one feels able to take what one wants from this kind of work. Nobody has to go the whole spiritual journey if they don't want to and, for the man in the street, this isn't always practical. For those of you who want to learn energy therapy for yourself and apply it to your horse, you can take basic training in a day and find a teacher quickly and easily.

I am aware that in writing this book I am in danger of having offended certain members of the healing community; perhaps the Reiki purists will say I'm adulterating their work, perhaps faith or spiritual healers will say that I should take a more religious approach to healing, other therapists may say I should have mentioned their kind of healing. If I have offended anyone, I sincerely apologise, because this was not my intention. What I have tried to do is simply to present what I know in a way that will be of practical use to people with horses, to give them a 'way in' without being too 'way out' about it. The direction that people follow once they have read this book is entirely up to them; we all have to find our own way. The main reason that I have not attempted to 'teach' through the pages of this book, or include specifics about what students will learn if they do decide to take training in energy therapy, is because a book cannot take the place of a teacher-pupil relationship. The way that teachers work is so varied that it is impossible for me to cover every method here, and besides, every teacher's individual experience varies.

Whatever approach you take, learning to use energy changes people's lives for the better and, as I am always saying, life is too short. Life is too short to be sick; life is too short to be negative; life is too short to be unhappy, or miserable, or angry, or to take our petty grievances out on the people or animals around us. Most of you will have a lot of positive things in life to be happy about – the eyes that read this book; the hands that hold it; the mind that understands it; the horse you're going to work on with it; the body that rides the horse – even the person who tells you to put the book down and come and do something else! We can all learn to place a little more emphasis on the positive things in our life, and less emphasis on the negative. Once we do, it's amazing how quickly we can gain the strength to handle the challenges that life can throw at us, and how insignificant the negatives actually become. It's also important to really live life to the full and to be happy. Perhaps there are aspects of your life that you would like to change – well, there's no better time to start than now. Perhaps energy therapy will give you the strength and motivation to make those changes.

I believe that it is time to start making some bigger changes, and breaking down the barriers that we have constructed within our own society. It is time to approach health care differently, and to stop placing a boundary between what is mind, what is body, and what is soul or other – all living beings are a whole entity, not a bunch of parts. It is time to discard labels about what is conventional and what is complementary – there already exists a doctor-healer network in the UK, so perhaps we can extend that principle to our animals and change the face of modern veterinary medicine. Many forward-thinking medics have trained or retrained in energy medicine. It is time to forget the 'us and them' approach to the care of people and animals, to learn from each other. It is high time to explode the myth surrounding the fact that healing is for the chosen few, and not the ordinary person. It's also time for us to stop making ourselves sick, and learn to make ourselves well.

References

1. *The Uncommon Touch*, Tom Harpur, McClelland & Stewart Inc, Canada, 1994.
2. *Quantum Healing*, Deepak Chopra, Bantam Books, USA, 1989.
3. *The Healing Arts*, Ted Kaptchuck and Michael Croucher, BBC Books, London, UK , 1986.
4. *You Can Heal Your Life*, Louise Hay, Hay House Publishers, Santa Monica, California, USA, 1984

Index

Page references in **bold** type refer to illustrations.